MACKINAC TREASURES

MACKINAC TREASURES

THE MUSEUM COLLECTIONS OF MACKINAC STATE HISTORIC PARKS

STEVEN C. BRISSON

MACKINAC ISLAND, MICHIGAN

50 YEARS
Historical Preservation
and Museum Programs
1958~2008

Mackinac Treasures
The Museum Collections of Mackinac State Historic Parks

by Steven C. Brisson
Chief Curator
Mackinac State Historic Parks
Mackinac Island, Michigan 49757

Design by Group 230, Lansing
Photographs by John Wooden

First Printing 3,000 copies

Library of Congress Cataloging-in-Publication Data

Mackinac State Historic Parks.
 Mackinac treasures : the museum collections of Mackinac State Historic Parks / Steven C. Brisson.
    p. cm.
 Includes bibliographical references and index.
 ISBN-13: 978-0-911872-89-7
 ISBN-10: 0-911872-89-2
 1. Mackinac State Historic Parks--Museums--Catalogs. 2. Mackinac State Historic Parks--Museums--History. 3. Material
culture--Michigan--Mackinac, Straits of, Region--Catalogs. 4. Material culture--Michigan--Mackinac Island (Island)--
Catalogs. 5. Mackinac, Straits of, Region (Mich.)--Antiquities--Catalogs. 6. Mackinac Island (Mich. : Island)--Antiquities--
Catalogs. I. Brisson, Steven C. (Steven Charles), 1967- II. Title.
 F572.M14M33 2008
 977.4'923--dc22
                                    2008032733

In Memory of
William H.B. Fritz
1961-2007

Tom Kachadurian

*For twenty-five years Bill served as con-
servator for the Mackinac Island State
Park Commission. He worked diligently
to upgrade and professionalize the care
of all of our collections. Bill's dedication, loyalty, and good humor are deeply
missed by all who knew him.*

CONTENTS

FOREWORD ix

INTRODUCTION 1

TREASURES 19

NATIVE AMERICAN COLLECTION .35

FORT MACKINAC 51

MACKINAC ISLAND AND MACKINAW CITY 77

BIBLIOGRAPHY. 161

ACKNOWLEDGEMENTS 163

INDEX. 164

FOREWORD

In the spring of 1976 I was hired as the first curator of collections for Mackinac State Historic Parks (MSHP). After working three summers as a seasonal tour guide at Fort Mackinac and completing my graduate work in museum studies, I began my professional career caring for MSHP's small but growing collection of historic objects. It was in this position that I developed an appreciation and understanding of the significant and foundational role of the museum collections in preserving and presenting the rich history of Mackinac.

Collecting historic objects is at the heart of every history museum's mission. MSHP collects for three purposes: to preserve, understand and interpret Mackinac history. We systematically collect historic objects in order to preserve the "material culture" of the Straits of Mackinac region. This includes everything from nails and newspapers to teapots and tools. Without this effort, we risk losing the physical remains that represent and define our past. These objects, which come from specific people, periods and places, teach us about our past. Each object in its own small way provides insight: nails reflect manufacturing processes; newspapers communicate the economic, political and social issues of the day; teapots represent style and taste; tools help define technological achievement, and

so on. When the stories of Mackinac are told through exhibits and displays, it is historic objects which illustrate, explain and give visual perspective to our interpretations of the past. These objects communicate form, function, texture, design and utility and join with labels and graphic images to communicate a fuller, more complete story. Photographic images of these objects are included in many of our publications in order to serve a similar illustrative purpose.

Professional collections management of Mackinac-related historic objects began 50 years ago when MSHP launched its historical preservation and museum program. In 1958 the Mackinac Island State Park Commission received authority to sell revenue bonds and use the proceeds to develop the historic sites within its parks. The commission was empowered to collect admission fees and other revenues at these historic sites in order to retire the bonds and maintain and develop professional museum preservation and interpretation programs.

From the beginning, a portion of this money was dedicated to collecting historic objects. Initial efforts were designed to simply provide materials for period settings and interpretive displays. In time, collecting activities evolved to include development of a collections policy, systematic acquisition efforts, creation of proper storage and display facilities to ensure preservation of the collections, and the professional museum management processes of cataloging, accessioning and inventory.

After a half a century, the results of the MSHP historical preservation and museum program have been remarkable. Fort Mackinac, once a crumbling, run-down, graffiti-filled old military post on Mackinac Island's southern bluff, has been completely restored. Several other Mackinac Island historical buildings have been restored and opened to the public. In addition, Colonial Michilimackinac, little more than charred ruins covered by beach sand in Mackinaw City, has been rediscovered through 50 years of archaeology and, today, nearly half of its buildings have been reconstructed. Likewise, the eighteenth-century sawmill and associated buildings at Historic Mill Creek Discovery Park have been archaeologically excavated and accurately reconstructed. All of these sites are brought to life with a wide array of informative and entertaining exhibits that feature historical objects which have been acquired through purchase and donation over the past half century.

Collecting and preserving is part of our public trust, a defining activity of Mackinac State Historic Parks. We are charged with this responsibility and empowered with the authority and resources to build and sustain an historical collection. Crucial to the success of this responsibility has been the steadfast support of the Mackinac Island State Park Commission and its leadership over the past 50 years. In commemoration of the 50th anniversary of our historical preservation and museum program, the commission is proud to share the treasures of our museum collection in this publication. Chief Curator Steven Brisson, who has managed and developed the collection for over a decade, has drawn from his comprehensive knowledge of these objects and their importance to the Mackinac story to provide the reader with a fascinating tour through Mackinac's museum collections.

Phil Porter, Director
Mackinac State Historic Parks
Mackinac Island State Park Commission

INTRODUCTION

Figure 1
Honorable Edwin O. Wood, LL.D. (1861-1918) in a painted photograph by Underwood & Underwood, ca 1916.
W 23.5 H 28, 1956.214.1

For centuries Mackinac has been a place to gather for Native Americans, French, British and Americans. They came for sustenance, commerce and pleasure. Mackinac was the location of summer fishing, missions, fur trading, military outposts, and summer vacations. The physical evidence of some of this activity is left behind. Uncovering select areas of this activity is the work of archaeologists. The artifacts they discover are pieced together to add to our understanding of lives once lived here.

Most artifacts, however, stay above ground and some survive through successive generations: documents, paintings, photographs, tools, and items of everyday life. Some remain at Mackinac while others leave with their original owners. Some of these objects continue to be used; others are eventually relegated to trunks, attics, or barns. Some artifacts may even become a revered and cherished reminder of a family's or a community's past. These objects can evoke an earlier age, bring it into clearer focus, and provide valuable information about our shared experiences. Properly understood and interpreted, they can be important and indispensable tools in telling the history of Mackinac and often provide a story in and of themselves.

An important part of the Mackinac Island State Park Commission's mission is preserving and interpreting the past. Gathering, caring for, and exhibiting historical artifacts is a critical activity in carrying out this mission. Today the commission's collection of artifacts and archival materials number over 20,000 individual specimens. Every year the commission continues to invest resources into the acquisition, preservation, research, and exhibition of this collection to benefit the thousands of visitors who come to our sites.

From its establishment in 1895, the Park Commission was aware of its role to preserve the history of Mackinac Island. Professional park management, historic preservation, and historical museums were in their infancy and there were few national examples and standards to follow. The commission's historical activities were focused on commemorating important events and individuals through the establishment of Marquette Park, the Nicollet Watch Tower, the Cass Memorial, and placing markers at Fort Holmes, the War of 1812 Battlefield, and to honor Dr. William Beaumont's groundbreaking studies in human digestion. The historical importance of Fort Mackinac was regularly acknowledged and, although most of the structures were converted to rental spaces, the public was still allowed access into the fort "preserved for the education and pleasure of the coming generations."[1] In 1909 the commission

also took charge of Michilimackinac State Park in Mackinaw City on the south side of the Straits of Mackinac. This park existed primarily for historic preservation purposes, originally established as a municipal park in the 1850s to preserve the site of eighteenth-century Fort Michilimackinac.

Gathering a collection of "relics" and exhibiting them to the public was a logical next step, which the commission first took in 1914. In that year the oldest building at Fort Mackinac, the Officer's Stone Quarters, was "set aside for the purpose and use of establishing a State Museum...."[2] It is not clear what, if anything, was first exhibited in the museum. In 1918 the commission accepted the personal collection of "relics and curios" of Commissioner Edwin O. Wood and instructed the park superintendent to install them "and such others as shall from time to time be contributed" into the Stone Quarters museum. The Wood Collection consisted of prehistoric arrowheads and stone tools and historical objects collected in southern Michigan. Wood, a Flint judge, was also a member of the Michigan Historical Commission and an amateur historian. He had a deep interest in Mackinac history, authoring the mammoth two-volume *Historic Mackinac* in 1918.

For the next several decades, other items were gathered for exhibition in this space. Part of this included material to document Michigan's role in the Great War. In 1919 the commission solicited Michigan's United States Senators and

Figure 2
Examples of the collection Commissioner Wood donated for the Fort Mackinac Museum. The bulk of the collection was purchased from the estate of collector Eugene J. Mathewson (1849-1912) of Portland, Michigan. Two fish weights, spear, ax head, large cutting tool, arrowhead; plates. U.1622 U.1996; plate, 1956.43.1, English ceramic; lamp, 1956.15.1, "Babbitt 2126"

members of Congress to obtain "relics of the war with Germany to be placed on exhibition at Mackinac Island State Park and Michilimackinac State Park."[3] It is interesting to note that Michilimackinac State Park was included in this original call, although at the time no venue existed in the park for the display of anything. However, just four years earlier landscape architect Warren H. Manning had completed a plan for the development of Michilimackinac. In addition to general park improvements, Manning suggested a reconstruction of the fort and the construction of a museum building adjacent to it.[4] While neither suggestion was immediately carried out, the commission completed a reconstruction of the fort in 1933 which eventually included a small "museum" building within it. This is further acknowledgment of the commission's understanding that the parks under its charge were important historical resources which should be interpreted for the public.

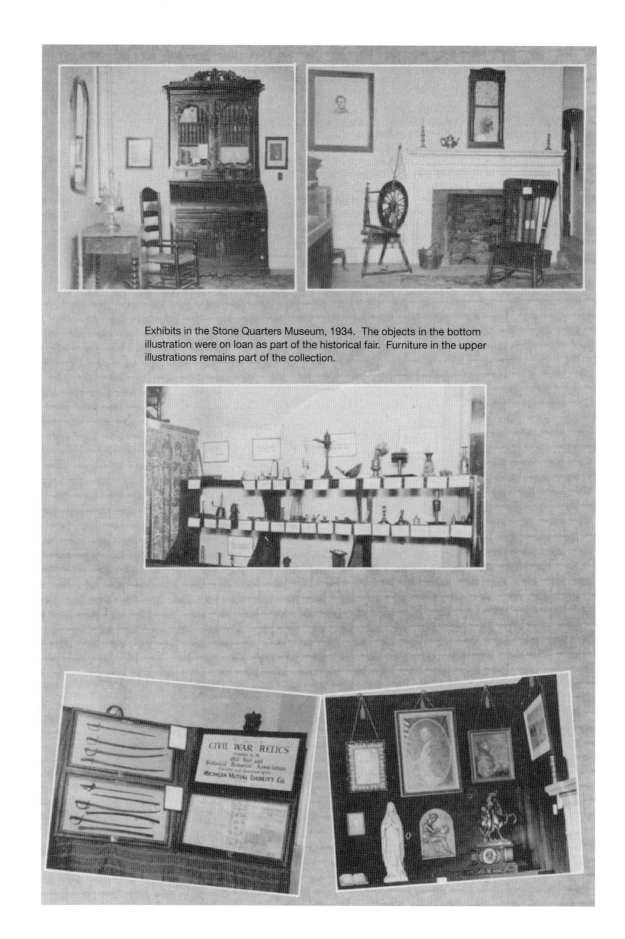

Exhibits in the Stone Quarters Museum, 1934. The objects in the bottom illustration were on loan as part of the historical fair. Furniture in the upper illustrations remains part of the collection.

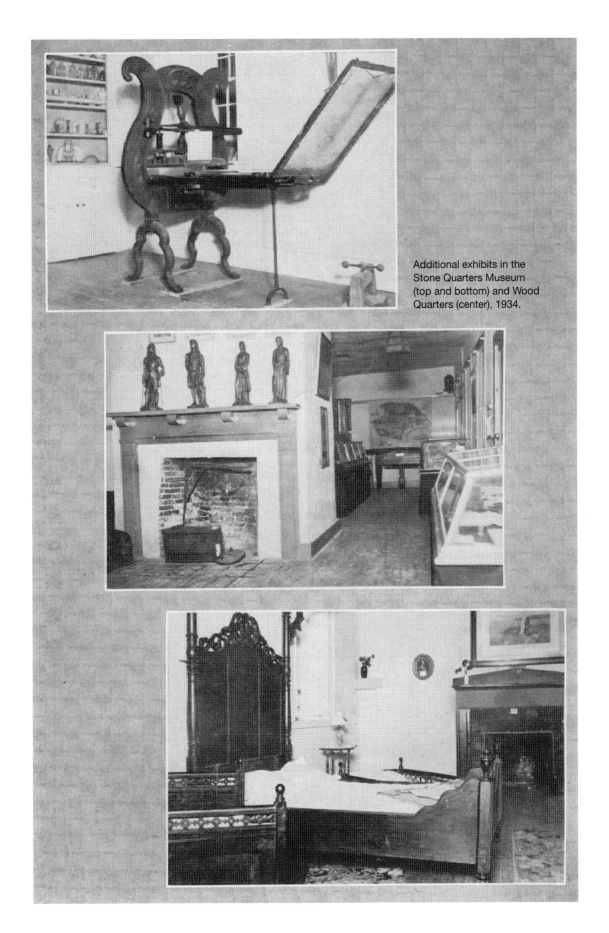

Additional exhibits in the Stone Quarters Museum (top and bottom) and Wood Quarters (center), 1934.

Figure 3
Relics of two World Wars from the
period when Stone Quarters served
as the state's military museum.
U.2489 German Helmet, U.2524
American Helmet,
U.2490 American Helmet

In its early decades, the Stone Quarters museum grew fitfully with the addition of the World War I artifacts (World War II artifacts would be added after 1945) and occasional other acquisitions directly related to Mackinac's history. However, the collection apparently did not receive adequate care. In 1933 Commissioner Roger Andrews reported that "the fort museum is a pitiful imitation of the real thing."[5] Over the next several years a program was launched to correct the situation. Exhibition space was expanded to the Wood Quarters and the large central rooms on the first and second floor of the Soldiers' Barracks. It was also better organized; period setting exhibits were added to Stone Quarters, and the objects were cataloged. In 1934 a "historical fair" was held which included

the exhibition at Fort Mackinac of numerous loaned objects from individuals throughout Michigan, as well as murals and dioramas from the Michigan exhibit at Chicago's Century of Progress Exposition. The main force behind all these improvements was Commissioner Andrews. He served on the commission three times from the late 1920s through the 1930s, twice as chairman, and also as acting park superintendent. Andrews had a keen understanding of the history of the Straits of Mackinac as well as the commission's obligation to present it. He was also aware that the history of the island was a great tourist draw. A resident of Menominee, Michigan, Andrews was managing editor of the *Menominee Herald-Leader* as well as the *Detroit Times*. Even when not on

Commissioner & Mrs. Roger Andrews (bottom row) with student winners of a commission-sponsored historical essay contest in 1936. The winners were treated to a visit to Greenfield Village including lunch with Henry Ford (center).

the commission, he was an active island booster and throughout the 1930s and 1940s published the summer weekly, *Mackinac Island News*, which included numerous historical articles. In 1938 he wrote *Old Fort Mackinac on the Hill of History*, giving the copyright and proceeds to the state. In addition to these projects in historical research and museum collections, he also launched the agency's first historical preservation and restoration programs. Through the assistance of the federal Works Progress Administration, the first professional study of Fort Mackinac's architecture, restoration of some of the buildings,

and the reconstruction of Fort Holmes were completed. Reading the reports and news stories of the day, it appeared as if the commission was on the threshold of a new age. In regards to museum collecting, Andrews was briskly fanning the flames that Commissioner Wood had ignited twenty years earlier. Unfortunately the fire did not spread and most of these programs, including ongoing improvement to the museum, faded by the 1940s. Faded, but did not die.

In the 1950s an interest in the historic value of the commission's sites and the collection was kept alive by Commissioner Margaret Price. In addition to acquiring Mission Church, a gift from the trustees of the property, the commission hired an expert from the Kalamazoo Public Museum to update the catalog of the Fort Mackinac collection.[6] Commissioner Price's interest in history was shared by another influential commissioner, "Ex officio" member, Governor G. Mennen Williams.

From the time he became governor in 1949, Governor Williams played an active role in Park Commission affairs. He possessed a keen interest in history, and by 1955 Governor Williams began to prod the commission to promote historical preservation issues. He planted a seed in November of that year by bringing together a blue ribbon group of commissioners and other interested parties and experts to discuss the state of historical preservation on the island. Following the meeting, while such issues began to appear more regularly on their agendas, the commission did not proactively continue these efforts. Governor Williams was not happy with the slow progress. Realizing he needed someone on the commission to actively pursue historical development, he appointed W. Stewart Woodfill, owner of Grand Hotel, to the commission and ultimately commission chairman. Woodfill shared the governor's enthusiasm for these issues. However, just the will to do things was not enough. It would take resources. Woodfill and Williams came up with the idea of selling revenue bonds to raise the necessary funds to launch a preservation and museum program. Entrance fees to the restored sites would be the source of revenue to retire the bonds. The act authorizing the Park Commission to sell bonds was passed in 1958. It also gave the commission broad authority to raise funds. This innovative way to preserve history succeeded beyond their wildest hopes.[7]

Dr. Eugene T. Petersen was hired as director of this new museum program. Working with his wife, Marian, and a small cadre of consultants including Victor Hogg, an artist and curator at Michigan State University Museum, and Dirk Gringhuis, a commercial artist and book illustrator and curator at Michigan State University Museum, Petersen transformed the commission's historic sites into engaging museums. A new interpretive exhibit was installed in Fort Mackinac in 1958. The following summer the archaeological excavation of Fort Michilimackinac was begun. The first reconstruction based on the findings was completed in 1960. Tens of thousands of visitors flocked to both forts. The Mackinac Island State Park Commission was now an agency dedicated to preserving history.

During the early years much of the effort was necessarily focused on building restoration and construction, developing interpretive programs, and exhibits. There was little emphasis on systematic collections acquisitions or care. The archaeological collection, growing each

Eugene Petersen reviewing archival material.

season, was processed according to the standards of the profession. The historical collection was different.

Dr. Petersen was aware of the need for material culture to interpret the history of the sites. He later noted that a search of Fort Mackinac turned up, apart from some original army plans and maps in the commission vault, only one original object: a chair.[8] The objects from the old fort museum, cataloged in 1937 and again in 1955, presented a somewhat eccentric gathering of relics and curiosities. Although there were a few gems within the various exhibits, the bulk of it consisted of non-provenanced arrowheads, china, and World War I memorabilia. Some antique furnishings

were exhibited in Stone Quarters, as well, from the period settings installed the 1930s. Further collections of furnishings had come with the recent acceptance of the Biddle House, developed by the Michigan Chapter of the American Institute of Architects. It was this last type of material, period furnishings, which was to dominate the collecting efforts of the 1960s and 1970s. It was driven by the need to furnish the buildings inside Fort Mackinac and the downtown buildings, including the Indian Dormitory, acquired in 1966. Initially Dr. Petersen acquired objects through the Marquette County Historical Society and the Edison Institute & Greenfield Village. The bulk of the period settings were eventually developed by antiques dealer Beulah Groehn of Detroit. Petersen hired Groehn in the off season to purchase all the necessary furniture and paraphernalia for a given location, such as the 1870s Post Headquarters. Groehn would purchase the needed objects, Petersen would review and approve them, and the objects would come up to the fort in the spring for installation. Groehn, with an expertise in antiques, also had a good eye for detail. Some of her installations are still in place at Fort Mackinac.

While there was little effort, or time for that matter, in developing the collection beyond what was needed for exhibit, a small collection of material with a Mackinac provenance was nonetheless assembled. There were, of course, the old objects from the Fort Mackinac museum, a few with a Mackinac provenance. Several other items of a similar nature were acquired. This was mainly due to the thousands of visitors coming to the sites. Among these visitors were descendents of Fort Mackinac soldiers and other Mackinac Island residents. Observing that the commission was now operating professional, highly-visible museums, they chose to donate heirlooms to the commission. The largest growth in targeted collecting activity in these early years was archival material, particularly photographs. Not only did Dr. Petersen have an interest in such items, but historical photographs were one of the best documents in helping

to accurately restore Fort Mackinac. Photos were also ideal for exhibits and in publications. The photos often entered the collection one at a time, but occasionally in larger groupings. The most significant photographic acquisition was the Gardiner glass plate negative collection in 1969. The collection consists of nearly 4,000 negatives of island views and portraits taken between 1896 and 1915. Dr. David Armour, a professional historian like Petersen, joined the staff in 1966. He shared Petersen's interest and appreciation in photographs and archival documents. Directly managing the museum operations of the commission for many years, Armour initiated several important acquisitions including the Gardiner collection, the Porter Hanks' sword, and the Deed to Mackinac Island.

Even though the majority of items being acquired were for period setting exhibits, there was still a need for storage and work space. In 1968 a "museum storage building" was constructed in the Mackinac Island State Park service yard. It consisted of work shops on the ground floor for exhibit and restoration projects and a storage area on the second. Although unheated and often used for the storage of non-collections materials, it provided a space for the objects from the old fort museum and new acquisitions deemed not suitable for exhibit.

Improving the commission's collections care and professionalizing this area of the operation began in earnest in the 1970s.

David Armour with the newly acquired Deed to Mackinac Island, 1983.

It was driven by improved standards within the larger museum world and the commission's interest in trying to live up to them. In 1972 the commission sought accreditation from the American Association of Museums. Since the 1937 and 1955 cataloging, little had been done with the new acquisitions since 1958. In order to ensure accreditation, Keith Widder, interpretation supervisor, and Brian Dunnigan, graduate student and summer curatorial assistant, worked

Phil Porter at work in the Museum Storage Building, 1978.

to catalog the entire collection. As the majority of items were on exhibit, this proved a daunting task. However, during the summers of 1972 and 1973, they successfully assigned accession numbers, marked the objects, and produced a minimal catalog card, most with a photograph of the object, in time for accreditation. It was reported to the commission that "the accessioning system now in use seems to be highly usable, and, with proper attention, it should provide a good base for further expansion and identification of the collection." An organization of the items in storage was also completed.[9]

With the urging of Keith Widder to bring on staff to care for the collection, Phil Porter, a former

Fort Mackinac guide who had recently completed his master's degree in museum studies, was hired in 1976 as the first curator of collections. The museum storage building was upgraded with the addition of an office, darkroom, and a climate-controlled special storage room to house the glass plate negative collection and other sensitive objects. A staff person focused on collections issues meant that for the first time the management of the collection would be systematic. Basic conservation treatment, records management, and exhibit planning were now actively pursued. Although Porter's title was eventually changed to curator of interpretation and he switched his focus to managing the interpretive and exhibit functions of the organization, collections

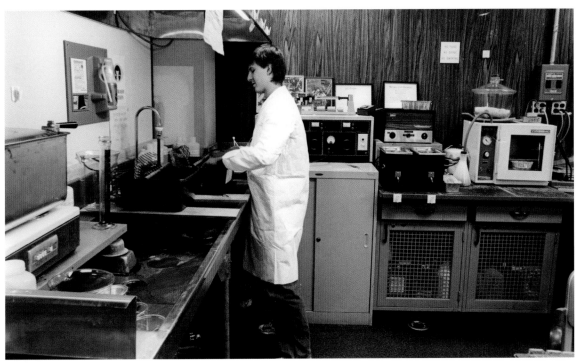

Conservator Bill Fritz at work in the laboratory, 1983.

care remained under his purview. Cataloging and other activities were largely completed during the summer by temporary staff.

The collections program continued to grow in the 1980s and 1990s. Again, as with the push to catalog the collection in the 1970s, this was often driven by a desire to live up to improved professional standards. A collections management policy was first adopted by the organization in 1981 (replaced by a new version in 1991 and updated in 2000). Director David Pamperin (1984-1990) and Director Carl Nold (1991-2003) each championed collections care issues in these decades. Critical assessments of the institution's collections were completed under Pamperin which resulted in the most sweeping improvements in

collections management that the agency had seen. An exhaustive survey of the collections was completed in 1989 through a federal Institute of Museum Services grant. The report included an assessment of the collections care practices and recommendations for improvement, which the commission began to immediately implement. A staff collections committee was appointed to guide collections planning and development. A new collections facility, the Heritage Center, was completed in 1990. Located next door to the old 1968 building, it provided three floors of climate controlled collections storage and work space. By the middle 1990s the collections staff included a curator, conservator, and registrar. The curators of collections included Jane Robinson, (1988-1989), Marsha Hamilton

(1990-1994) and Steven Brisson, hired in 1996 and becoming chief curator in 2004. Bill Fritz, who had worked as a crew member on the Michilimackinac archaeology dig, was hired full time in 1983 as conservator for the archaeology collection. By the late 1980s his role had expanded to encompass the historical collection as well. Preventative maintenance issues in exhibit areas became a key concern and Fritz worked diligently to compile environmental data in all areas housing collections and adjusting conditions wherever possible. This included such measures as filtering windows for ultraviolet radiation and developing tightly-sealed exhibit cases containing environmental buffers for sensitive objects. Jennifer Lis was hired as conservator in 2008. The first collections registrar was Linnea Aukee Nurmi (1994-2000) followed by Michelle Hill (2001-2006) and Brian Jaeschke, hired in 2006. The addition of the registrar position allowed for more systematic and thorough record keeping, which was greatly enhanced by the computerization of the records in 1994-96. The registrar also tends to the commission's Petersen Center Library. The small but tightly focused research center began during the Petersen era as an assemblage of research materials for staff use. Keith Widder, in his later role

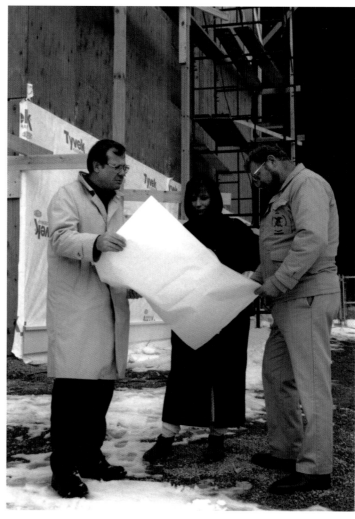

David Pamperin, Marsha Hamilton, and Park Manager Donald Francis reviewing plans for the Heritage Center, 1991.

as curator of history, both organized and expanded the library holdings. The collection is discrete from the archival holdings and today contains 15,000 books, manuscripts, microfilms, periodicals, photographic copy prints, and related materials. Developed for staff use, the library has for years been available to outside researchers.

With staff in place and collections management under control, greater emphasis and resources were now devoted to collections development. Under

Registrar Linnea Aukee Nurmi marking new acquisitions, 1999.

Director Carl Nold, commission policy was updated to ensure that the Collections Committee review and recommend new acquisitions with final approval by the Park Commission. A Museum Assessment Program collections survey, building upon the 1988 findings, was also completed in 1993. Money was annually budgeted for collections acquisitions. Several premiere objects, namely the DePeyster Bowl and Dashwood Painting, were acquired through special fund-raising efforts. A tightly focused scope of collections helped to guide collections acquisition planning. While collections are still acquired for use in particular exhibits, including period settings, there is now a priority in searching for and acquiring

objects with a Mackinac provenance. Since 1996 an average of 100 new accessions are processed annually, varying between 200 and 700 individual objects per year. In 2001 a second collections facility, the Petersen Center, was completed in Mackinaw City. The facility houses the archaeological collection, library and conservation laboratory, functions that until then were located in the commission's Lansing office. The lab is used for the treatment of both archaeological and historical artifacts.

In 2003 Phil Porter became director. Since the 1970s he had been involved with the development of the collection and implementation of sound collections management practices. In that same year, Martin and Patricia Jahn, long time supporters of the parks, generously donated a collection of historic maps documenting the history of Great Lakes cartography. Dating from the sixteenth through the nineteenth century, ten of the twenty maps were added to the collection. As the Jahns allowed the remaining ten to be sold, Porter took this opportunity to use the proceeds to establish a permanent collections development fund, named in honor of the Jahns. The development fund represents the ongoing commitment of the Park Commission to enhance and protect the museum collection.

In 2007 the Park Commission successfully received its third reaccreditation by the American Association of Museums. Unlike 1972, when accreditation was first granted, no effort was needed to bring the parks' collections program in line with professional standards. The accreditation committee acknowledged that Mackinac State Historic Parks lives up to the professional standards of a museum. A staff guides the care of the collection. Policies and procedures are in place and implemented to ensure the utmost care of the artifacts. Records are carefully attended to and automated. Proper measures in exhibition spaces and state-of-the-art storage facilities ensure the preservation of the objects. There are, of course, areas for improvement in the care and control of the collections. These are regularly addressed in the commission's long-range planning process. Through revenue bond financing, the support of outside donors, grant agencies, and Mackinac Associates, the numerous improvements of the last several decades were accomplished. The acquisition of new objects to fill gaps in the collection also continues. The commission can point with pride to the efforts made, especially in the last four decades, to bring its museum collection into the vanguard of historical site museums in the United States. The treasures of Mackinac are secure for present and future generations.

---

1   Mackinac Island State Park Commission, *Mackinac Island State Park, Report of the Board of Commissioners*, 1909:31.

2   Mackinac Island State Park Commission Minutes of Meetings, 21 July 1914.

3   Ibid., 26 July 1919.

4   Warren H. Manning , "Mackinac Island State Park Commission, Michilimackinac Park, Mackinaw City, Mich., Study for Arrangement of Roads and Paths," Boston: Project No. 1072, 1915.

5   Mackinac Island State Park Commission Minutes of Meetings, 10 March 1933.

6   David Armour, *100 Years at Mackinac* (Mackinac Island: Mackinac State Historic Parks, 1995), 72.

7   Ibid., 74-78.

8   Eugene Petersen, personal communication to author, 1996.

9   Brian L. Dunnigan, "Curator's Report" Summer, 1972; "Curator's Report" 1 September 1973.

TREASURES

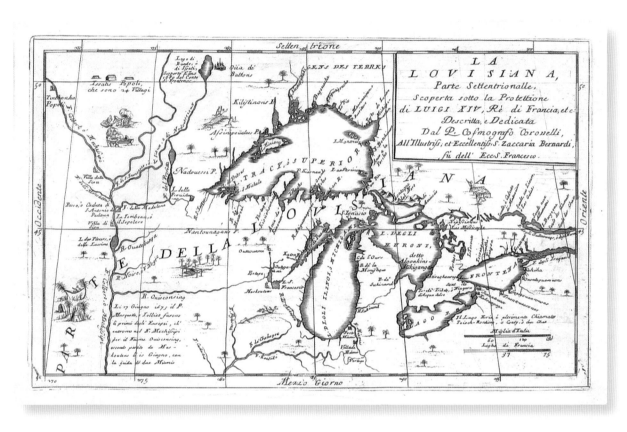

Coronelli, a French cartographer for Louis XIV, receives credit as the first person to show the Great Lakes accurately and in their relative positions. Coronelli had access, through Louis XIV, to the latest manuscript maps of French explorers and priests.

Figure 4
La Louisiana, **Coronelli**
1690
W 18 H 12
2003.31.2
Martin and Patricia Jahn

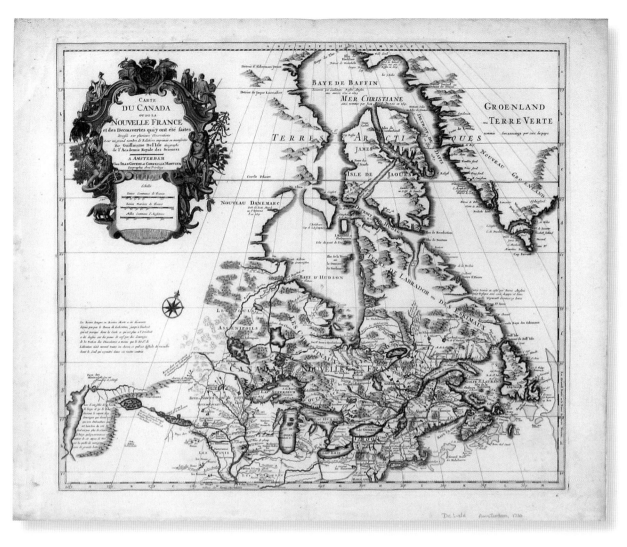

*Map shows improved delineation of the Great Lakes
over earlier maps. Lake Michigan is labeled "Lac Illinois"
and Lake Huron is "Michigane."*

Figure 5
Carte Du Canada ou de la Novelle France,
Guillaume DeLisle
ca. 1717
W 23 H 19.75
2003.31.3
Martin and Patricia Jahn

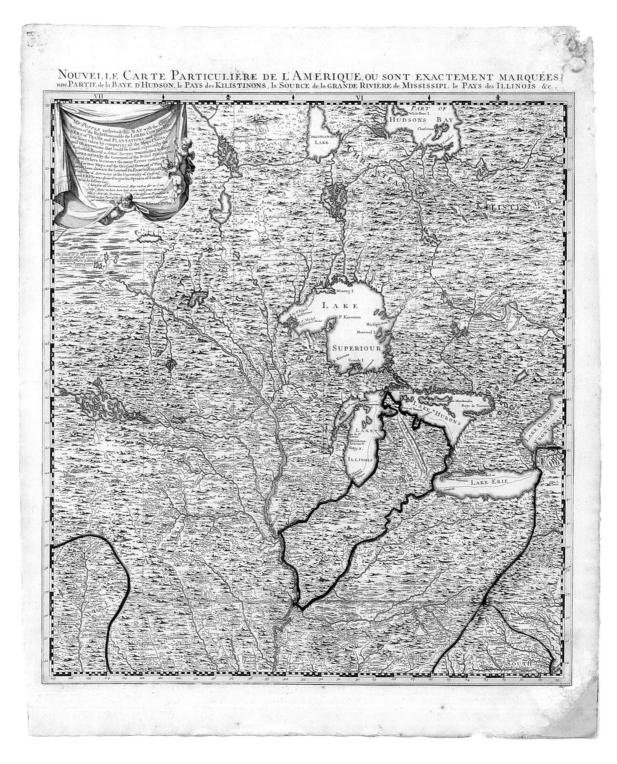

The map, with unusual shapes for Lakes Superior and Ontario, also includes a "high plain" in Michigan.

Figure 6
Nouvelle Carte de Particuliere de L'Amerique,
Henry Popple
1733-1740
W 21 H 23
2003.31.5
Martin and Patricia Jahn

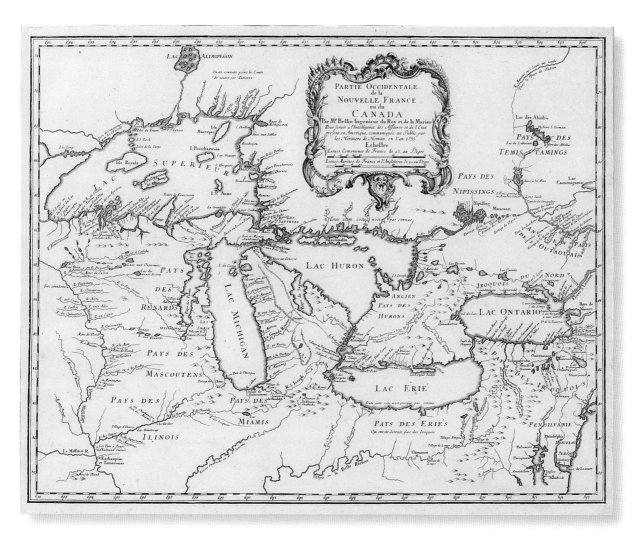

A cartographic landmark of the region. Noteworthy for the introduction of the islands in Lake Superior, which remain on maps for nearly a century. The map summarizes the French knowledge of the region and shows the river systems discovered by French explorers, forts and settlements, and Indian villages. The chart incorporates the work of Sieur de La Verendrye, the last of the great French explorers in North America. First issued by Bellin in 1745 and re-issued by the Homann Heirs on the eve of the French and Indian War.

Figure 7
Partie Occidentale de la Nouvelle France ou du Canada,
Jacques Nicolas Bellin Issued by Homann Heirs
W 21 H 17
2003.31.6
Martin and Patricia Jahn

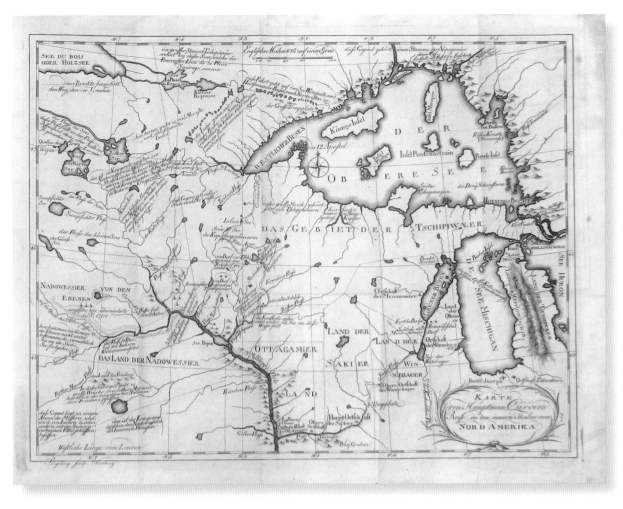

Map showing North America at the time
of the American Revolution.
Lake Superior contains three non-existent islands.

Figure 8
Partie Occidentale du Canada et Septentrionale de la
Louisiane avec une partie de la Pensilvanie, D'Anville
1775
W 22.5 H 19
2003.31.7
Martin and Patricia Jahn

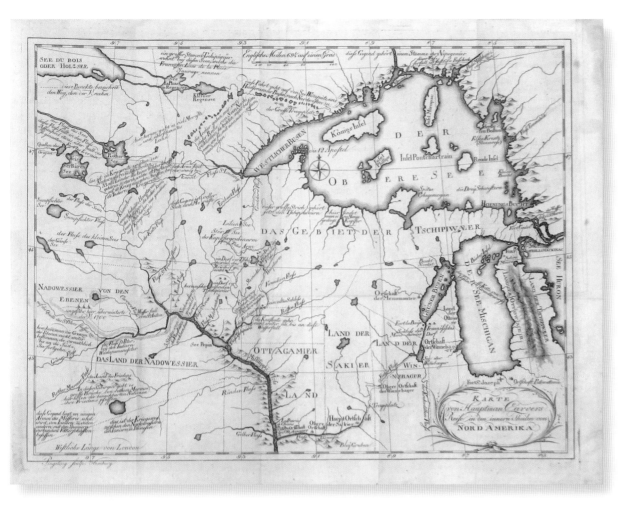

German-language version of map of Captain Jonathan Carver (1710-1780) of his 1766-67 travels showing Michigan, Wisconsin, and portions of Minnesota. The English version was first published in 1778. Various areas of the map are labeled with the names of the Native Americans who lived there. Among represented locations are Fort Michilimackinac and to the south "Askin's Farm."

Figure 9
Karte von Hauptman Reisse in den innern Sheilen von Nord Amerika
ca. 1780
W 14.5 H 11.5
2004.85.1
Martin and Patricia Jahn

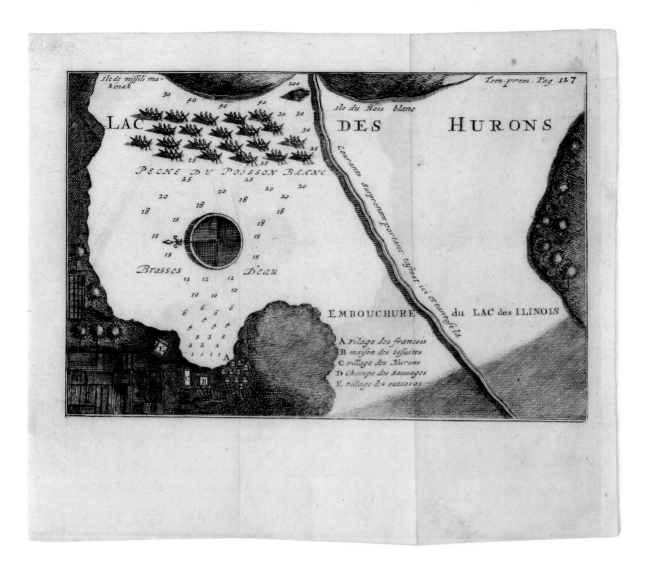

Captain Louis-Armand de Lom d'arce de Lahontan depicted the settlement at St. Ignace in 1688. This is a ca. 1705 version of his map that first appeared in his 1703 book, New Voyages to North-America *(as the later English translation was known). North is to the left on the map.*

Figure 10
Lac des Hurons, **L. A. Lahontan, Amsterdam**
1705
W 7.125 H 6.125
1986.25.1

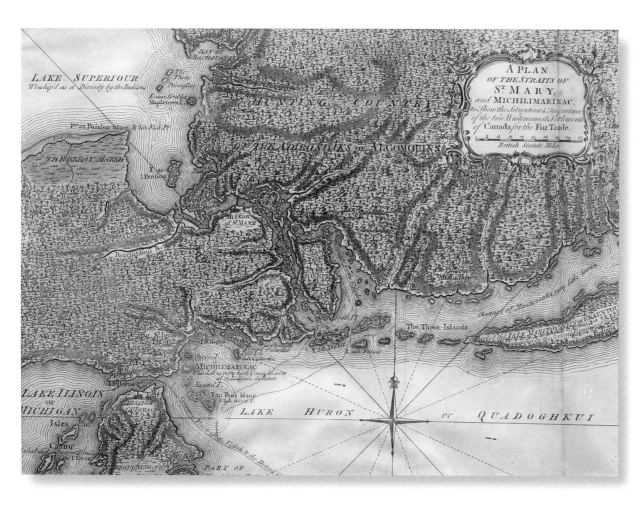

This early English view of the Straits of Mackinac and St. Mary's River shows details of the surrounding area and the relationship of the Straits to the surrounding lakes. The map was based on earlier French maps, notably the one by Bellin (Figure 7).

Figure 11
***A Plan of the Straits of St. Mary and Michilimackinac to Show the Situation & Importance of the two Westernmost Settlements of Canada for the Fur Trade,** The London Magazine: Or, Gentleman's Monthly Intelligencer*
1761
W 14 H 10
1985.114.1

In 1828 John Mullett (1786-1862) completed an official land survey of Mackinac Island. The survey recorded for the first time fifteen private claims of property on the island. In the following years numerous copies were made from the original map in the General Land Office in Washington that was produced as part of the survey. This is one of two manuscript copies in the commission's collection. It was made in 1845 and "sent to Capt. [Silas] Casey at Fort Mackinac."

Figure 12
***Michilimackinac I. Showing the Surveys of Private Claims*, J. Mullet**
1828
W 21.25 H 27.25
2007.61.1
Clayton Timmons

A superb example of neo-classical silver, this sterling silver bowl was made in 1779-80 by Daniel Smith and Robert Sharp, among London's premier silversmiths. It was ordered in 1779 by the traders of Michilimackinac for their departing commandant, Arent Schuyler DePeyster. One cartouche carries a presentation statement in English, lauding DePeyster for his "just and upright conduct" and the encouragement he gave to trade. The other carries an image of "Michilimackinac," the Great Turtle with the French inscription "I remember Turtle, that for six years you were my only portion in life." The bowl is symbolic of the peoples that came together at Michilimackinac as well as the global connections of the fur trade.

Figure 13
DePeyster Punch Bowl
1780-81
H 12 D (top) 14.9 D (base) 8.9
1999.34.1
Purchase made possible by donors to acquisition fund drive.

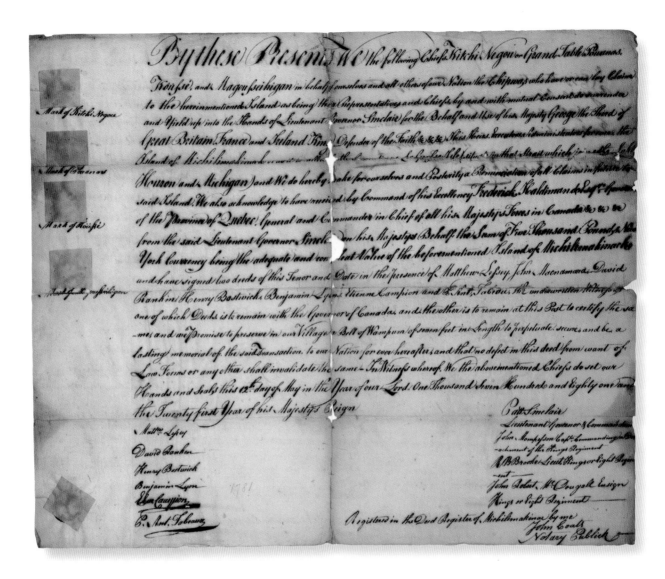

Figure 14
Deed to Mackinac Island
1796
W 18 H 14
1983.281.1
Martin and Patricia Jahn

With war in the colonies and fear of an attack by American rebels, the decision was made in 1779 to move Fort Michilimackinac from its vulnerable location on the southern mainland to the high bluff of Mackinac Island. British commandant Patrick Sinclair began negotiations with the resident Ojibwa to secure legal title to the island. The final transfer occurred in a formal ceremony on May 12, 1781. A deed was drafted and marked with the signatures of the English and totems of the Ojibwa. The original is at the Clements Library, University of Michigan. A second copy, which appears here, was drafted in 1796 when the United States took formal possession of the island from the British. On the reverse of this document is written: "I certify that the within is a true copy of the original deed in my possession, which was [delivered] me by the commander of Michilimackinac when I relieved him. H. Burbeck, Major and Commanding, Michilim. [sic] September 4th 1796."

The oldest known painting depicting Mackinac Island, by William Dashwood, was commissioned by Lieutenant Colonel Robert C. McDouall (1774-1848) in the 1820s. McDouall was British commander of Fort Mackinac during the War of 1812. The work commemorates his success in repelling the American attack during the Battle of 1814 and his capture of the American ships Tigress and Scorpion. These ships are seen being brought into Haldimand Bay with the British red ensign flying triumphantly over the Stars and Stripes. The view is based on the print Michilimackinac on Lake Huron by Richard Dillon, originally published in 1813. The artist has added several additional Native Americans, also drawn from contemporary prints, the captured vessels, and, to the left, McDouall in the distinctive green uniform and plumed shako of the Glengarry Light Infantry Fencibles. He is pointing proudly to the war booty sailing into the bay.

Figure 15
***Mackinac Island,* William Dashwood**
ca. 1820-29
W 22 H 16
2000.60.1
Anonymous (2), Clark Bloswick, Jean Taylor Federico, Todd Harburn, Bart Huthwaite, Martin D. Jahn, Mackinac Island Community Foundation, Carl Nold, Phil Porter, Mark E. Schlussel

Oil-on-velvet theorem painting with outlines stenciled and filled with paint. Hannah White was a sister of Amanda Ferry whose husband William operated the Protestant mission on the island. Hannah joined the group in about 1830 and taught at the mission school as late as 1834. Her perspective of Mackinac Island, although distorted, accurately depicts the southern portion of the island during the waning days of the fur trade. Many of Mackinac Island's landmarks are easily identifiable, including the buildings of the American Fur Company on Market Street, Fort Mackinac, the LaFramboise House, Ste. Anne's Church, Mission Church, Mission House, and Robinson's Folly. Indian wigwams and canoes line the harbor. Hannah White later gave the painting to her niece, Amanda Ferry Hall, who brought it back to Mackinac Island in 1911 and donated it to the trustees of Mission Church. It came to the Park Commission with the transfer of the church property in 1955.

Figure 16
Untitled View of Mackinac Island, **Hannah White**
ca. 1830-34
W 19 H 12.5
1997.00.27
Trustees of Mission Church

Fort and Island of Mackinaw. C. F. Davis Del. 1839.

In August 1839 Detroit artist Caleb F. Davis visited Mackinac Island and completed this pen and ink drawing on paper. Viewed from the south, it shows Fort Mackinac and the village. The new Indian Dormitory is prominently visible to the right below the fort. It was part of the federal Indian Agency and completed following the 1837 Treaty of Washington. The treaty was necessary as Michigan was on the verge of statehood and large portions of the territory were transferred from the tribes to the United States. It represents a time of great change on Mackinac Island. The days of the fur trade were over, fishing the main activity, and the days of tourism just beginning.

Figure 17
Fort and Island of Mackinaw, **Caleb F. Davis**
1839
W 10 H 8.25
1985.14.1
Mrs. Fred Dickson, great-granddaughter of the artist

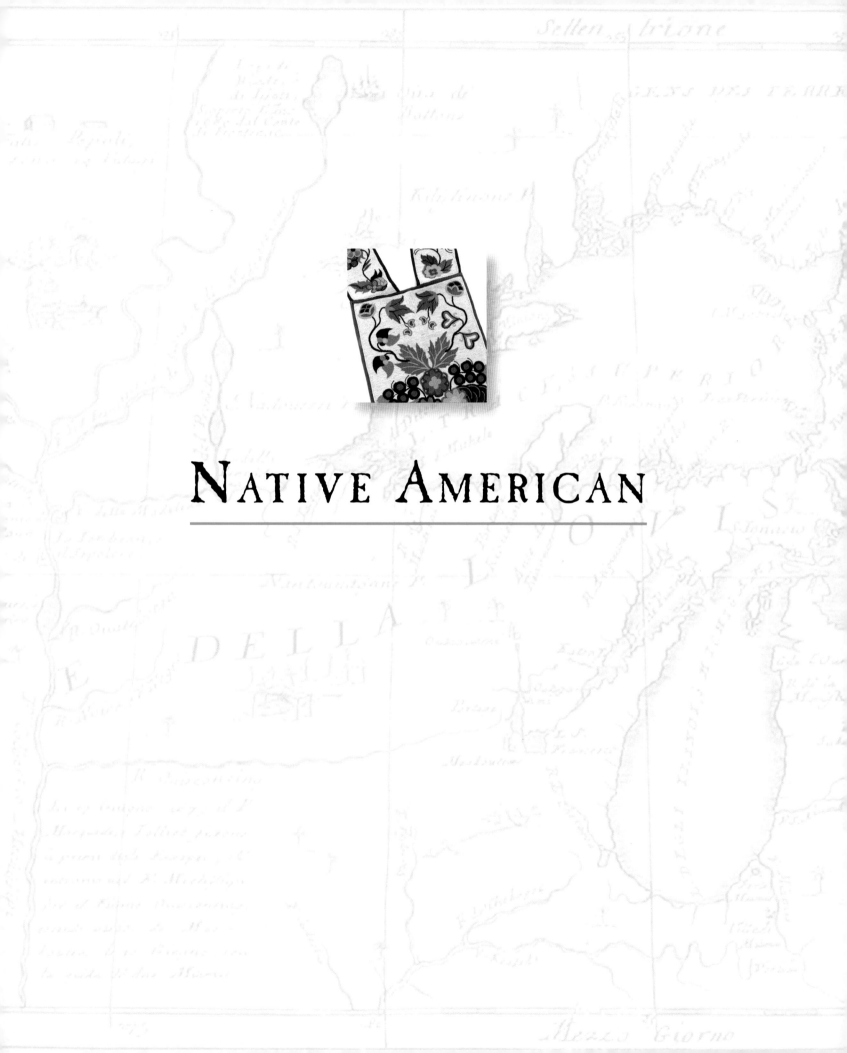

NATIVE AMERICAN

Habit of an Ottawa an Indian Nation of N. America.

Indien de la Nation Ottawa dans L'Amerique septentrional.

197

Figure 18
Engraving, "Habit of an Ottawa an Indian Nation
of N. America"
W 8.125 H 11.25
1985.105.1

Eighteenth-century engraving of an Ottawa warrior.
The Ottawa occupied a village on the north side of the
Straits of Mackinac near where Marquette established his
mission in 1671, relocating to the south side in the early
eighteenth century. Their main village in this region was
eventually L'Arbre Croche, near Cross Village.

Habit of a Woman of the interior parts of North America.

Figure 19
*Engraving, "Habit of a Woman of the interior parts
of North America"*
W 8.25 H 13. 25
1985.102.1

Figure 20
Indian Rattle
Dakota
ca. 1830
L 6.75
1978.5.1

Native American rattle composed of rawhide head filled with trade beads and wooden handle covered with red woolen cloth, decorated with red, white and green yarn. Obtained at Mackinac by member of Mackinaw Mission. Donated to the Connecticut Historical Society by Rev. William Ely prior to 1850. Purchased by the commission from Guthman Americana in 1978.

Figure 21 *(Facing page)*
Born in Syracuse, New York, Henry C. Gilbert (1818-1864) settled in Coldwater, Michigan where he worked as a lawyer. From 1853 to 1857 he served as federal Indian Agent for Michigan. He traveled considerably, but occasionally he and his family lived at the Indian Agency on Mackinac Island. He negotiated several treaties, including the Treaty of 1854 at La Pointe, Wisconsin. During the Civil War he organized the 19th Michigan Infantry and served as colonel. He was killed from a chest wound sustained at the Battle of Resaca, Georgia in 1864.

The 1854 Treaty of La Pointe was between the United States and representatives of the Ojibwa of Lake Superior and the Mississippi. The treaty ceded the entire Lake Superior Ojibwa lands in the Arrowhead Region of Northeastern Minnesota to the United States in exchange for reservations for the Lake Superior Ojibwa in Wisconsin, Michigan, and Minnesota. Gilbert received a number of personal gifts during the treaty, which were passed down to his descendants.

Figure 21
Photograph of Henry C. Gilbert
ca. 1862
W 2.25 H 8.25
1973.506.1
Budd Tompkins, descendent

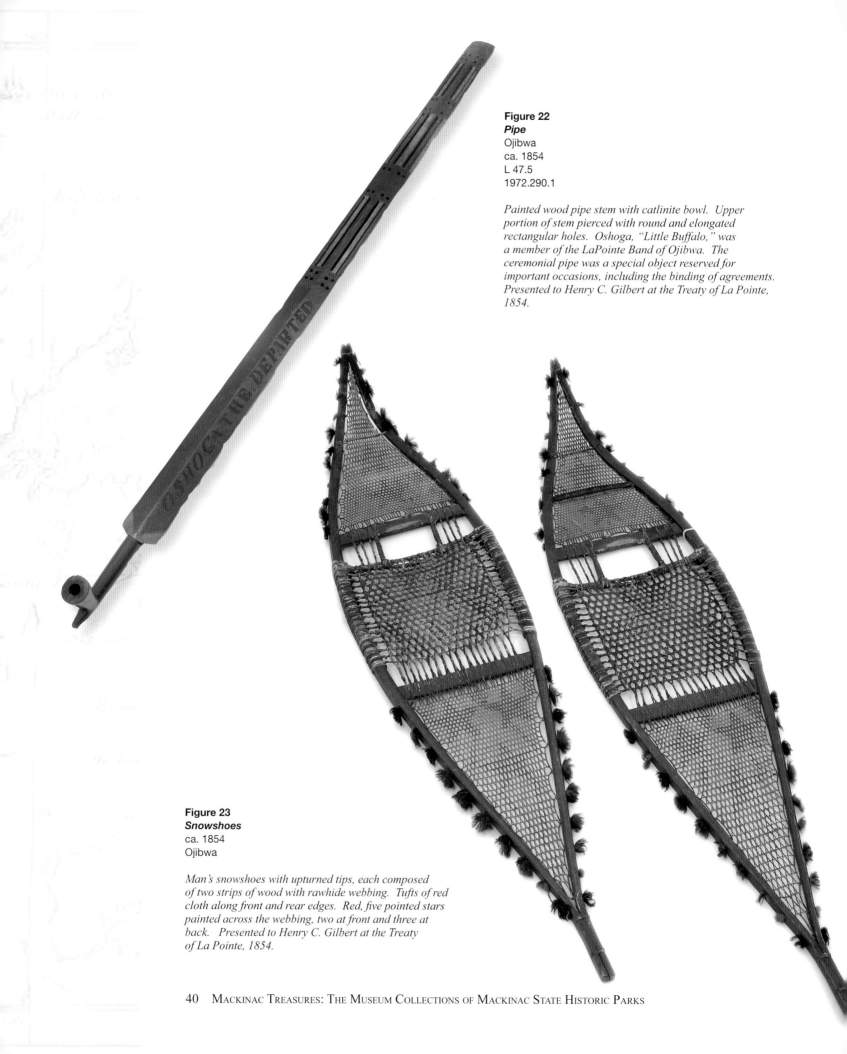

Figure 22
Pipe
Ojibwa
ca. 1854
L 47.5
1972.290.1

Painted wood pipe stem with catlinite bowl. Upper portion of stem pierced with round and elongated rectangular holes. Oshoga, "Little Buffalo," was a member of the LaPointe Band of Ojibwa. The ceremonial pipe was a special object reserved for important occasions, including the binding of agreements. Presented to Henry C. Gilbert at the Treaty of La Pointe, 1854.

Figure 23
Snowshoes
ca. 1854
Ojibwa

Man's snowshoes with upturned tips, each composed of two strips of wood with rawhide webbing. Tufts of red cloth along front and rear edges. Red, five pointed stars painted across the webbing, two at front and three at back. Presented to Henry C. Gilbert at the Treaty of La Pointe, 1854.

Figure 24
Cradle Board
ca. 1854
Ojibwa
L 29 W 12.5
1972.257.1
Budd Tompkins, descendent

Headboard and fender bar decorated with incised floral designs representing a blending of Ojibwa and European motifs. Presented to Henry C. Gilbert at the Treaty of La Pointe, 1854.

Figure 25
Bandolier
ca. 1850
Ojibwa
L 34 W 15
1972.262.1
Budd Tompkins, descendent

The Ojibwa shoulder bags came in different forms, serving both utilitarian and ceremonial functions In the final phase of development, shoulder bags became primarily decorative, as in this example, with a flat beaded panel replacing the pouch. The panel and straps are decorated with loom-woven beadwork. Small seed beads in a great variety of colors and cotton warps and wefts were used to make a complex, bilateral, and symmetric design. Presented to Henry C. Gilbert at the Treaty of La Pointe, 1854.

This man's shirt is made from manufactured calico. By the early decades of the nineteenth century most Native American women in the Great Lakes region preferred to make garments with manufactured material acquired through trade. Combined with imported decorative materials, they were shaped into distinctive Indian garments. This example features a front panel and cuffs decorated with woven beadwork in a floral design. Presented to Henry C. Gilbert at the Treaty of La Pointe, 1854.

Figure 26
Shirt
ca. 1854
Ojibwa
1972.293.1
Charles. L. Woodward, descendent

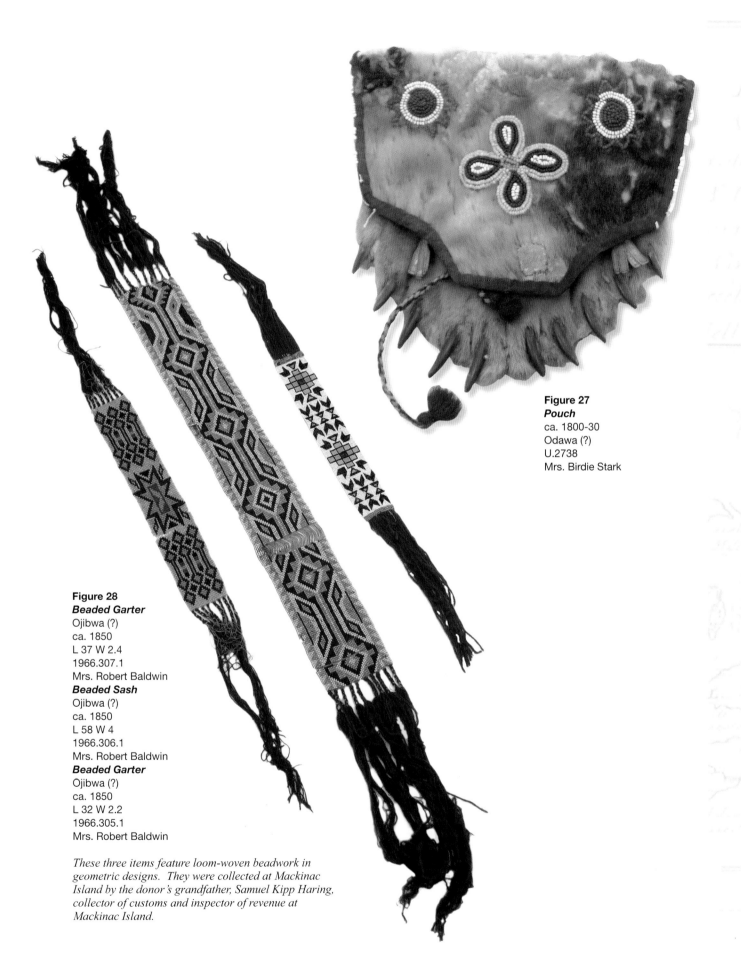

Figure 27
Pouch
ca. 1800-30
Odawa (?)
U.2738
Mrs. Birdie Stark

Figure 28
Beaded Garter
Ojibwa (?)
ca. 1850
L 37 W 2.4
1966.307.1
Mrs. Robert Baldwin
Beaded Sash
Ojibwa (?)
ca. 1850
L 58 W 4
1966.306.1
Mrs. Robert Baldwin
Beaded Garter
Ojibwa (?)
ca. 1850
L 32 W 2.2
1966.305.1
Mrs. Robert Baldwin

*These three items feature loom-woven beadwork in
geometric designs. They were collected at Mackinac
Island by the donor's grandfather, Samuel Kipp Haring,
collector of customs and inspector of revenue at
Mackinac Island.*

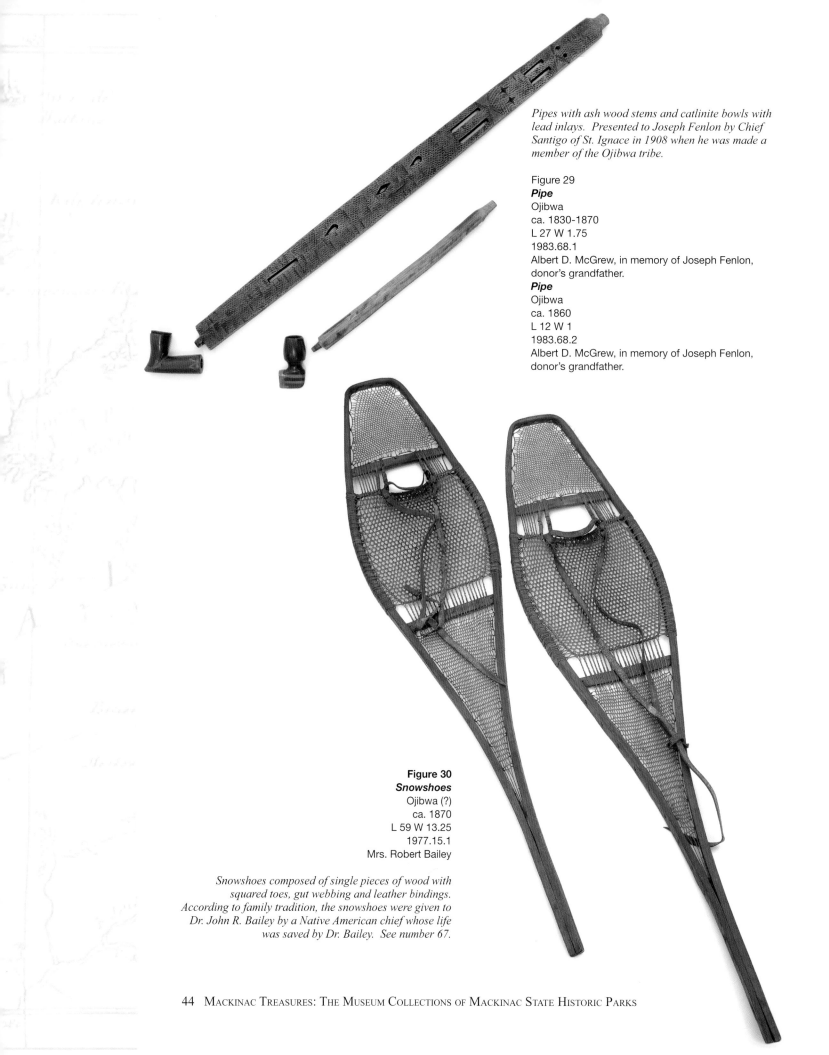

Pipes with ash wood stems and catlinite bowls with lead inlays. Presented to Joseph Fenlon by Chief Santigo of St. Ignace in 1908 when he was made a member of the Ojibwa tribe.

Figure 29
Pipe
Ojibwa
ca. 1830-1870
L 27 W 1.75
1983.68.1
Albert D. McGrew, in memory of Joseph Fenlon, donor's grandfather.

Pipe
Ojibwa
ca. 1860
L 12 W 1
1983.68.2
Albert D. McGrew, in memory of Joseph Fenlon, donor's grandfather.

Figure 30
Snowshoes
Ojibwa (?)
ca. 1870
L 59 W 13.25
1977.15.1
Mrs. Robert Bailey

Snowshoes composed of single pieces of wood with squared toes, gut webbing and leather bindings. According to family tradition, the snowshoes were given to Dr. John R. Bailey by a Native American chief whose life was saved by Dr. Bailey. See number 67.

Figure 31
Moccasins
Ojibwa or Odawa
ca. 1860
1972.272.1
Buckskin moccasins lined
with checked cotton.
Beaded cloth vamps and
ankle flaps.

Moccasins
Ojibwa or Odawa
ca. 1860
1972.271.1
Child's buckskin moccasins lined
with linen. Beaded black cloth
vamps and ankle flaps.

Moccasins
Ojibwa
ca. 1854
1973.504.1
Charles L. Woodward, descendent
Child's buckskin moccasins with quill appliqué
on vamp and ankle flaps. Presented to Henry
C. Gilbert at the Treaty of La Pointe, 1854.

Figure 32
Moccasins
Ojibwa or Odawa
ca. 1850
1972.289.1
Buckskin moccasins with beaded vamp.

Moccasins
Ojibwa
ca. 1854
1973.508
Budd Tompkins, descendent
Buckskin moccasins with beaded cloth vamps.   Presented
to Henry C. Gilbert at the Treaty of La Pointe, 1854.

Figure 33

Quill work on birchbark was a traditional Native American art form. By the latter nineteenth century these traditional techniques were used to create souvenir art specifically for the tourist trade.

Souvenir Canoe
Ojibwa
ca. 1854
L 15.5 W 5.8
1972.270.1
Charles L. Woodward, descendent
Presented to Henry C. Gilbert at the Treaty of La Pointe, 1854.

Souvenir Canoe
Ojibwa
ca. 1854
L 14 W 4.75
1972.243.1
Charles L. Woodward, descendent
Presented to Henry C. Gilbert at the Treaty of La Pointe, 1854.

Pouch
Ojibwa
ca. 1854
1973.503.1
Charles L. Woodward, descendent
Presented to Henry C. Gilbert at the Treaty of La Pointe, 1854.

Basket
Ojibwa
1972.260.1
Oval birchbark box with lid, heavily decorated with dyed quill.
ca. 1854

Pouch
1973.512.1
Budd Tompkins, descendent
Beaded buckskin pouch with cloth top. Presented to Henry C. Gilbert at the Treaty of La Pointe, 1854.

Canoe
U.2213
ca. 1940

Canoe
U.2212
ca. 1940

Figure 34
Birchbark Basket
1997.99.1
Mackinac Island
ca. 1920
Round birchbark box with lid and
decorated with sweetgrass and
natural colored porcupine quills.

Basket
U.2232
ca. 1940
Round box with lid, with interweaved
materials.

Souvenir Teepee
ca. 1940
1997.12.3
Souvenir small birchbark and wood teepee,
marked "Mackinaw City, Vada Imhoff."

Birchbark Basket
1939
U.2214
Urn-shaped basket with porcupine quill decoration, dated
"1-4-39."

Birchbark Bowl
1973.700.1
ca. 1940

Birchbark Box
Cynthia Norton
1939
U.2235
Dyed porcupine quills in a traditional design. Probably
completed as part of the federal Works Project
Administration Art and Craft Project. The box is signed by
Cynthia Norton and dated "1-17-1939."

Birchbark Box
Cynthia Norton
1939
U.2234
Dyed porcupine quills in a traditional design. Probably
completed as part of the federal Works Project
Administration Art and Craft Project. The box is signed by
Cynthia Norton and dated "4-11-1939."

Charles B. Fenton (1834-1925) came to Mackinac Island
in the 1850s. He operated a store with island merchant
Jacob Wendell and married Wendell's daughter, Elizabeth,
in 1858. By the 1870s he opened "Fenton's Bazaar."
The prominent souvenir shop consisted of a two-story
building with a mansard-roofed corner tower with shops
below and a hall, "Fenton's Opera House," above (see
the trade card in Figure 130). Fenton sold a variety
of souvenirs from his shop including birchbark items
decorated with dyed porcupine quills. This example was
likely displayed in the shop.

Figure 35
Quillwork and Birchbark Souvenir Canoe
ca. 1890
L 42.5
1991.13.2
Elizabeth Menner

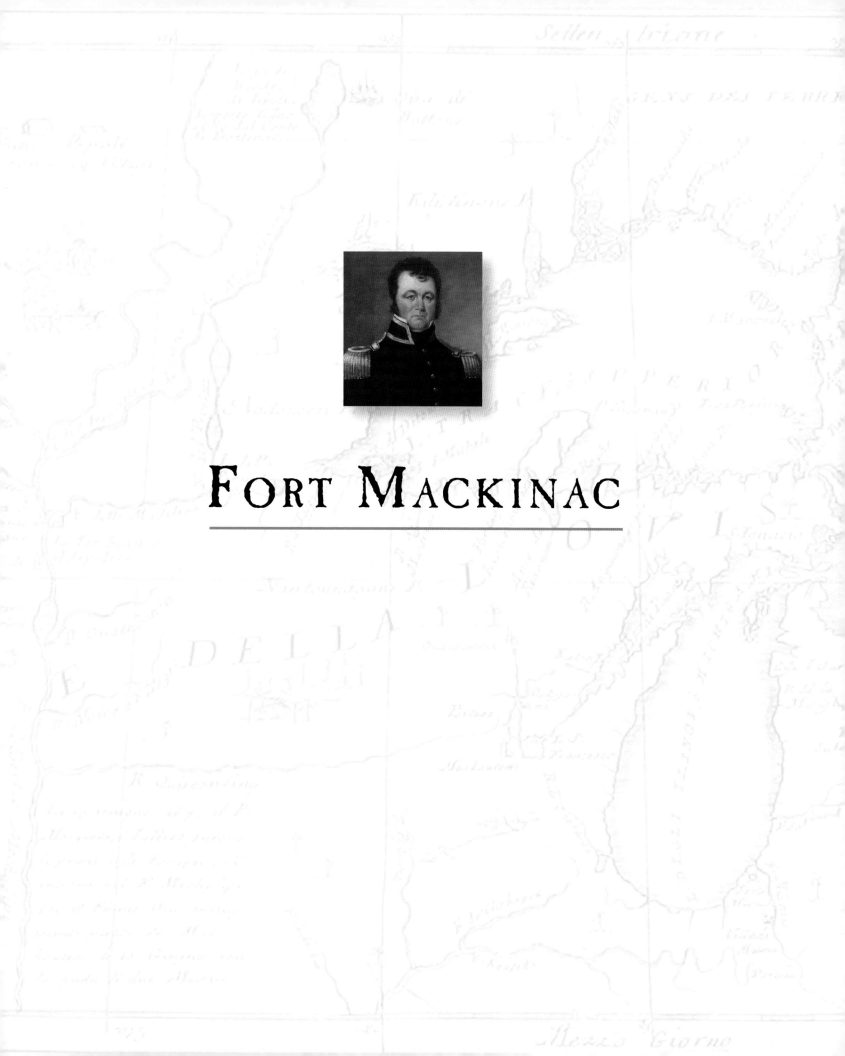

FORT MACKINAC

Figure 36 A-B
Porter Hanks Sword
L. Wells & Co., New York
ca. 1805-1812
1985.8.1-2
Ms. Kay Kendall-Krapill

Sword of American commander of Fort Mackinac, 1st Lieutenant Porter Hanks, Artillerists. Hanks was forced to surrender the fort to the British on July 17, 1812. He was killed less than a month later by a cannon ball in the British attack on Detroit.

Figure 37
Perry Cannon
L 99 D 13
1992.8.1
Transfer, Department of Natural Resources

Cannon barrel from either the Niagara *or* Lawrence.
American Commander Oliver Hazard Perry used these two naval ships during his victory in the 1813 Battle of Lake Erie. One year later United States forces used the Niagara *and* Lawrence *in their assault on Mackinac Island. A "twelve pounder" (fires a twelve pound iron ball), this cannon returned to Mackinac Island in the mid 1800s. For more than one hundred years the "Perry Cannon" was displayed on the shore in front of Fort Mackinac (see Figure 99). In the 1990s it was conserved and reinstalled in an exhibit at Fort Mackinac.*

Presented to the Fort Mackinac military museum in 1927. The drum was made by Charles Munger, Sr. and carried by him through the War of 1812. His son, Jeremiah Cutler Munger, carried it as a member of the Company E, 23rd Michigan Infantry through the Civil War.

Figure 38
Munger Drum
H 11.25 D 16.5
1956.219.1
Luna Freeland, Abbie Munger Beach, Ella A. Drew, daughters of Jeremiah Cutler Munger

In 1938 Wyeth Laboratories commissioned a series of paintings entitled "Pioneers of American Medicine." Fort Mackinac's post surgeon Dr. William Beaumont's studies of the stomach of Alexis St. Martin were the subject of one of the paintings. Beaumont's 1820s landmark investigtions were among the earliest American medical research recognized internationally and the foundation for human digestive study. This is a preliminary sketch by Cornwell of the central characters.

Figure 39
Beaumont and St. Martin, Paper and Pencil Sketch
Dean Cornwell
1938
W 17.75 H 14
1972.140.1

This is a preliminary oil sketch of the complete painting. The original painting is still owned by Wyeth, although it was on loan and exhibited at the commission's Beaumont Museum for several decades. This oil sketch was given by Dean Cornwell to the donor's father, Douglas John Withington, who worked for Wyeth for forty-two years.

Figure 40
Beaumont and St. Martin, Oil Sketch
Dean Cornwell
1938
W 23.25 H 18.5
2007.30.1
Paul Douglas Withington

William Whistler (1783-1863) entered the army in 1801. He spent most of his military career on the Great Lakes at posts such as Chicago, Detroit, Green Bay, and Niagara. Whistler served at Fort Mackinac three times, 1816, 1823 and 1833, the last two as commandant. He retired in 1861 as a full colonel after a record-setting 60 years in the army.

This portrait of Whistler was likely done while he was commander at Fort Niagara, New York. In 1833 it would have come with him to Fort Mackinac and hung in the Officers' Stone Quarters. Artist Grove Shelden Gilbert (1805-1885) was a native of New York. He worked in western New York and Ontario as a teacher and portrait artist. The painting, pistols, and pectoral descended through the Whistler family to his great-grand daughter, Miss Elida Clench, who sold them in the late 1960s to a St. Catharines, Ontario antiques dealer.

Figure 41
Portrait of Major William Whistler
Grove Shelden Gilbert
ca. 1831
H 30 L 35
2007.4.1
Purchase made possible by gift from Mackinac Associates and donors to associate-sponsored fund drive.

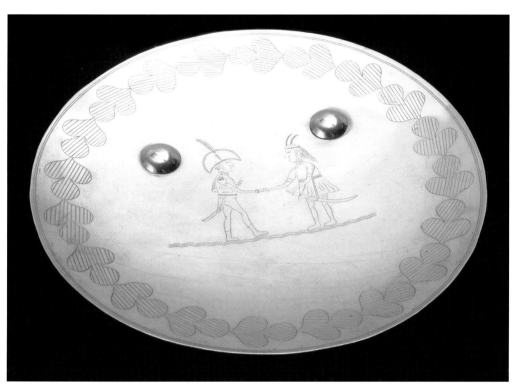

Figure 42
Silver Pectoral owned by William Whistler
ca. 1827
D 7.75
2007.4.3

*The image commemorates the surrender of Winnebago
Chief Red Bird to Whistler, then commander at Green Bay,
during the "Winnebago War" of 1827.*

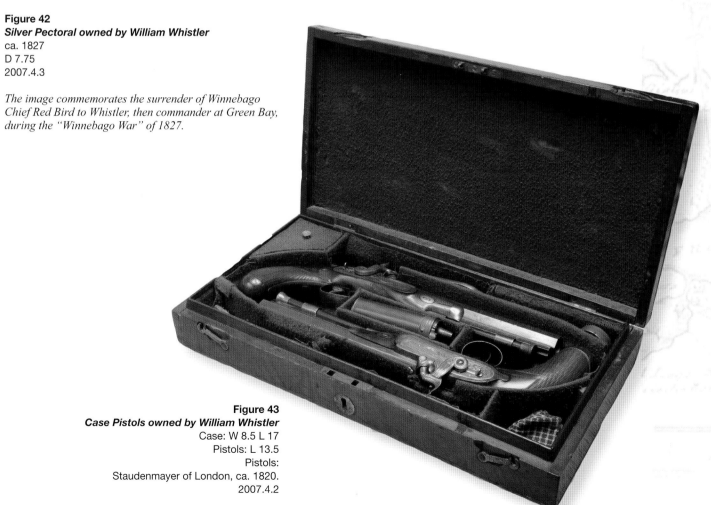

Figure 43
Case Pistols owned by William Whistler
Case: W 8.5 L 17
Pistols: L 13.5
Pistols:
Staudenmayer of London, ca. 1820.
2007.4.2

Bell-crowned, 1821-pattern leather cap.
This was the dress cap of the American soldiers
stationed at Fort Mackinac from 1821-1832
during the height of the fur trade.

Figure 44
Leather Dress Cap
ca. 1830
H 15.75 W 10.25
1960.102.1

Figure 45
Charlotte O'Brien Tintype
W 6.25 H 8.25
2003.28.1
ca 1860 tintype from an 1848 daguerreotype
O'Brien Nicholas Young, descendent

Charlotte Tull O'Brien (1812-1855)
was the wife of Fort Mackinac chaplain
Rev. John O'Brien. She was born in Berkshire,
England and came to Monroe, Michigan in 1832
with her family. There she met and married John,
who became chaplain at Fort Mackinac in 1842.
They lived and raised their family at Hill Quarters
until Charlotte's death thirteen years later.
She is buried in the Post Cemetery.

Figure 46
John O'Brien Daguerreotypes
ca. 1848-1860
2003.28.2
W 2.75 L 2.9
2003.28.3
W 3.25 L 3.75
O'Brien Nicholas Young, descendent

John O'Brien (ca.1806-1864) was born in Ireland.
He remained as chaplain at Fort Mackinac after
Charlotte's death until the troops were withdrawn at the
start of the Civil War. He obtained a parish in Pontiac,
Michigan and died from a stroke in 1864.

Figure 47 A-C
O'Brien Spoons
George Doty, Philadelphia
1835-45
2007.75.1-5
O'Brien Nicholas Young, descendent

Three of the spoons are engraved with John O'Brien's monogram and two that of Charlotte O'Brien. These items, though mundane, were nonetheless treasured and preserved by the O'Brien descendents. The O'Brien collection also includes archival material including John and Charlotte's letters (the basis for the book The Chaplain's Lady)*, John's sermons, and letters to John from his son, Lyster, while he served in the Civil War.*

Figure 48
William Marshall Envelopes
1864 and 1865
U.216, U.221

The "Old Sergeant," William Marshall (1823-1884)
was at Fort Mackinac for 36 years, longer than any
other soldier. Arriving in 1848, he served until his death.
During the Civil War he was the sole occupant of the
fort when the rest of the garrison was withdrawn to the
battlefields. These official army envelopes date to
the Civil War.

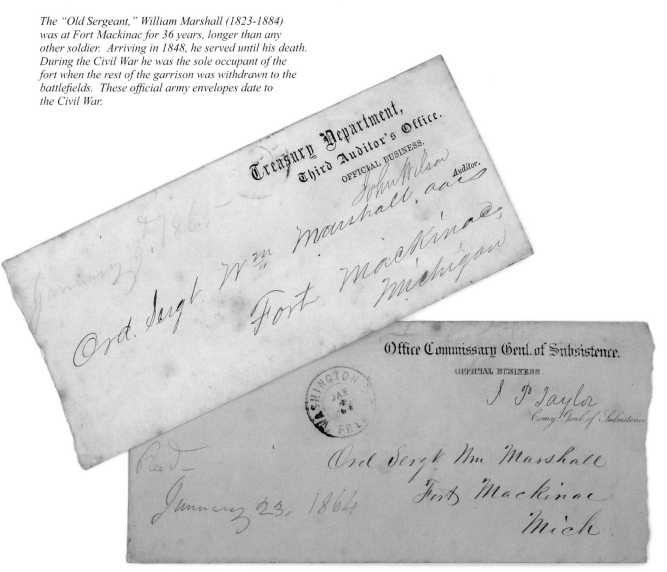

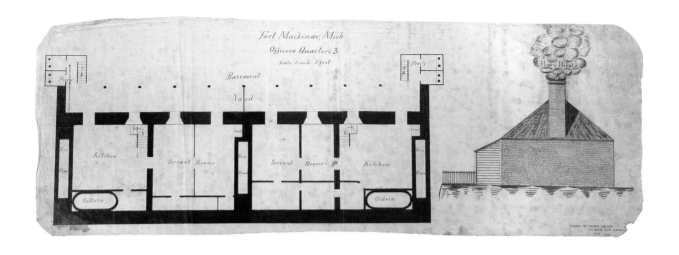

When the army vacated Fort Mackinac in 1895 they left behind plans of the fort for the Park Commission. Most of the plans are for buildings constructed late in the military period or showing alterations, such as this plan for Stone Quarters, originally built in 1780. Designed as a duplex officer's quarters, it served that purpose throughout the military period.

Figure 49
Officers Quarters 3, Ground Floor Plan and East Elevation
Henry Heintz
1875
L 33.5 W 12.25
2000.00.126

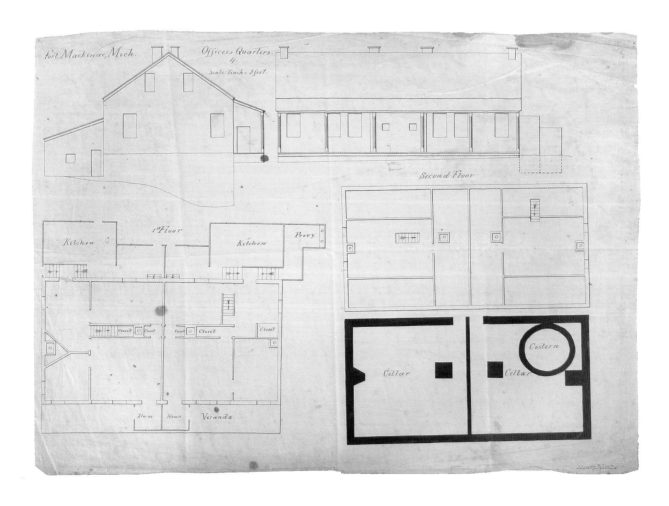

Figure 51 (below)
Sergeants' Quarters East Bay Addition, Plan Elevations
1885
L 25 W 20
2000.00.136

*By the second half of the nineteenth century, Fort
Mackinac had grown far outside its original walls.
Sergeants' Quarters was one of these structures,
constructed to the north of the fort in 1877.
This plan shows an 1885 addition to the building.*

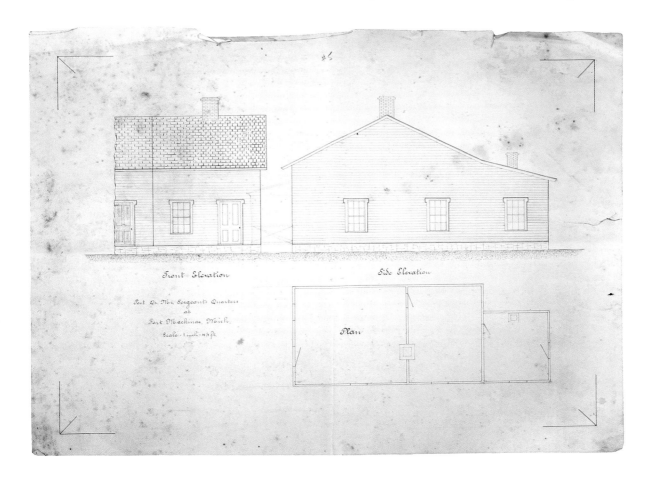

Figure 50 (at left)
Officers Quarters 4, Plans and Elevations
Henry Heintz
1875
L 26.3 W 20.9
2000.00.139

*Overlooking the parade ground, this duplex was home to
many officers and their families. Originally constructed
in 1835, this plan of the Hill Quarters was completed just
prior to a major remodeling in 1875. Sergeant Henry
Heintz, a native of Rohrbach, Germany served at Fort
Mackinac in 1874-75.*

Figure 52
Webb Calling Card and
Marriage Announcement
1998.00.21.1
1878

Less than a year after arriving at Fort Mackinac, Captain Charles Webb married Rosa Truscott Disbrow, a twenty-five-year-old widow, daughter of island merchant George Truscott. Unfortunately, Rosa became a widow again. In 1882, two years after leaving Fort Mackinac, Charles died of pneumonia. Rosa returned to Mackinac Island and devoted herself to community and charitable activities.

A wedding gift of the Webbs consisting of a hot water pot, coffee pot, tea pot, cream jug, waste pot, and covered sugar bowl. All the pieces are engraved "Rosa."

Figure 53
Webb Silver Service
Middletown Plate Co.
1878
1985.2-7
David Truscott Dort, descendent

John Fletcher served as Fort Mackinac's quartermaster
from 1885 to 1893. Photographs such as these help us
put a human face on one-time occupants of our historic
buildings. They also provide valuable details used for
restoration. Note the "storm house" attached to the front
porch, a protection against bitter winter winds; the built-
in roof ladders to reach the chimneys; and the rain barrel.
Mrs. Fletcher has nurtured some attractive geraniums in
improvised pots. Behind the front door is an apartment
that consisted of three rooms for the five occupants.
Figure 51 shows the apartment at the opposite
end of this building.

Figure 54
***Fletcher Family in Front of Sergeants' Quarters
Apartment***
ca. 1890
W 6.5 L 8.875
1989.4.14
Robert J. Fletcher, descendent

Figure 55
Fletcher Chevrons
ca. 1885-1893
W 8.5 H 6.75
1989.4.17
Robert J. Fletcher, descendent

Sergeant Fletcher's chevrons, one of which is visible in the previous photograph.

Figure 56
Fletcher Chair
ca. 1885
1989.4.21
Robert J. Fletcher, descendent

If we could go through the door in Figure 54, it is likely we would find this chair, one of a set.

From 1879 to 1884, 1ˢᵗ Lieutenant Dwight Kelton (1843-1906) served at Fort Mackinac. Mackinac Island was then a fashionable summer resort, and had been made the country's second national park four years before Kelton's arrival. An enterprising man, Kelton used his spare time in researching and compiling a guide book for island tourists. The Annals of Fort Mackinac was first issued in 1882 and went through twelve editions.

Figure 57
Cabinet Card and Calling Card of Dwight H. Kelton
1964.7.1
1964.7.2
Mrs. James T. Bond

Figure 58
Kelton Sofa
ca. 1840-1870
1973.537.1

In 1889, one year after retiring from the army, Kelton returned to Mackinac Island and married his sweetheart, Anna Donnelly. They settled in his hometown of Montpelier, Vermont. After Kelton's death in 1906 Anna returned to Mackinac Island where she lived until her death in 1934. This sofa was part of her estate.

Figure 59 (opposite)
Pratt Album
1880-1910
1990.26.1
Violet Bowling, descendent

Lieutenant Edward Pratt (1853-1923) of the Twenty-third Regiment of Infantry served at Fort Mackinac from 1884-1889. He had spent part of his boyhood at Fort Mackinac, when his father, Captain Henry C. Pratt, commanded the post from 1858 to 1861. His grandfather, John D. Clitz, also commanded the post from 1834 until his death in 1836. Edward brought with him his wife, Kate, and only child, Mary. This photo album records the family's life at Fort Mackinac as well as other posts throughout the country where the Pratts were stationed. The album contains numerous photos of Mackinac Island and Fort Mackinac including a view of the Pratt's parlor in Stone Quarters and the interior of the Soldiers' Barracks (seen here). These are two of only three interior views of Fort Mackinac in the military period known to exist.

Figure 60 (above)
Corbusier Curios
2004.137.1-8
Joseph Porter

The son of post surgeon Dr. William H. Corbusier, Harold Corbusier (1873-1950) spent part of his boyhood at Fort Mackinac from April 1883 to September 1884 and again in 1892. These relics of Fort Mackinac's past were collected by Harold and treasured away in a cardboard box. His daughter, Nancy Corbusier Knox, presented them to Joseph Porter when he portrayed Harold Corbusier in a reading from Harold's published diary, A Boy at Fort Mackinac.

Morse Collection

Born in Macon, Missouri, Benjamin Clarke Morse (1859-1933) later moved with his family to Marquette, Michigan. He graduated from the United States Military Academy at West Point in 1884. His military career in the U.S. Army Infantry lasted over 40 years, with distinguished tours of duty in the Philippines, Cuba, Vera Cruz, and Panama and as commandant of cadets at Texas A&M and the University of Illinois. He retired a brigadier general in 1920. Morse's first tour of duty was Fort Mackinac in 1884-1890. In 1890 he married Jessie A. Cable on Mackinac Island, whose father owned the John Jacob Astor House Hotel.

Figure 61
Cadet Jacket of Benjamin C. Morse,
West Point Military Academy
1880-1884
1993.9.11
B. C. Morse, III, descendent

Figure 62 A-B
Officer's Sword of Benjamin C. Morse
ca. 1890
L 40.5
2003.53.1
William Morse, descendent

Saber for cavalry and mounted officers of infantry,
1872 Pattern. This pattern was often used by other
officers, as evidenced by this example.

Figure 63 (below)
Dress Sword Belt and Box of Benjamin C. Morse
ca. 1890
1993.9.4.a-b
B. C. Morse, III, descendent

Japanned tin boxes were sold by military suppliers for the
storage of either belts or shoulder knots.

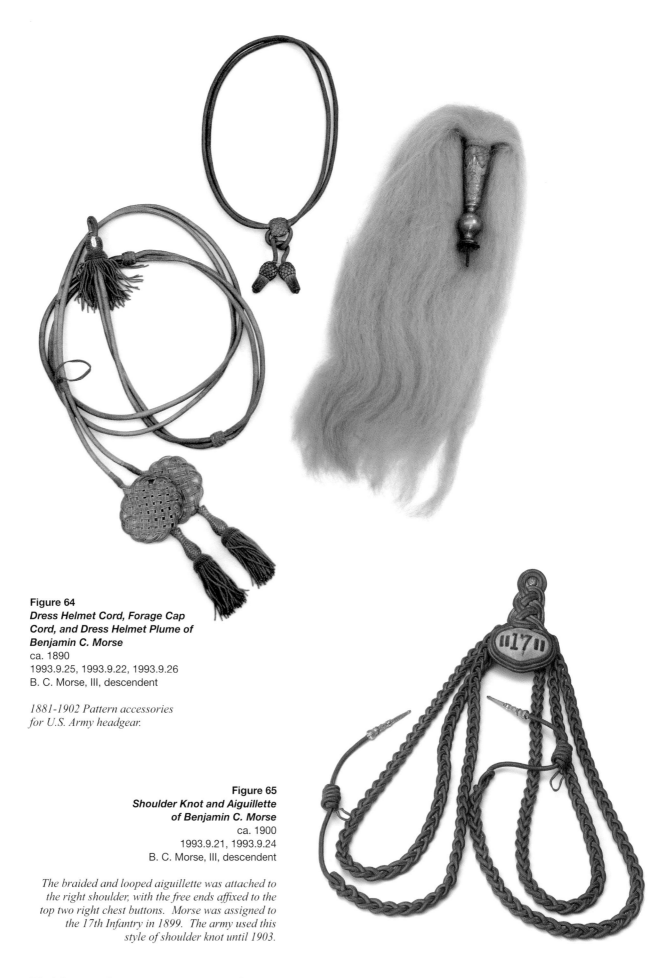

Figure 64
Dress Helmet Cord, Forage Cap
Cord, and Dress Helmet Plume of
Benjamin C. Morse
ca. 1890
1993.9.25, 1993.9.22, 1993.9.26
B. C. Morse, III, descendent

1881-1902 Pattern accessories
for U.S. Army headgear.

Figure 65
Shoulder Knot and Aiguillette
of Benjamin C. Morse
ca. 1900
1993.9.21, 1993.9.24
B. C. Morse, III, descendent

The braided and looped aiguillette was attached to
the right shoulder, with the free ends affixed to the
top two right chest buttons. Morse was assigned to
the 17th Infantry in 1899. The army used this
style of shoulder knot until 1903.

Figure 66
Benjamin C. Morse Medals
1884-1917
Benjamin Clarke Morse, Jr.

33rd Regiment of Infantry Rifles
1984.606.1
*Morse commanded the 33rd from August 1918
to July 1920.*

"American Occupation Vera Cruz, Mexico 1914"
Campaign Medal
1984.591.1
*Morse served at Vera Cruz from October to
November 1914.*

13th Regiment of Infantry
1984.603.1
Morse transferred to the 13th in 1915.

Major Insignia
1984.620.1
Morse held the rank of major from 1907 until 1913.

"Philippine Insurrection 1899" Campaign Medal
1984.590.1
*Morse completed two tours of duty in the Philippines,
1898 and 1899.*

**Bronze-colored metal eagle used on olive drab and
khaki caps from 1902-1923.**
1984.595.1

Brigadier General Insignia
1984.596.1
*On August 5, 1917 Morse was promoted to Brigadier
General of the National Army. He returned to the rank
of Colonel of the Regular Army in 1918, but retired a
Brigadier General in 1920.*

Colonel Insignia
1984.597.1
*Morse was promoted to Lt. Colonel of Infantry in 1913
and full Colonel in 1916.*

World War I "National Army" Collar Insignia
1984.608.1
*Officers in command of the National Army (the drafted
forces) of World War I wore these collar insignia,
authorized from mid-1917 until 1918.*

17th Regiment of Infantry, Regimental Quartermaster
1984.603.1
Morse was assigned to the 17th on January 1, 1899.

23rd Regiment of Infantry
1984.598.1
*Morse wore this insignia while stationed at Fort
Mackinac. He served with the 23rd from 1884 until 1890,
from 1894 to 1899, and again in 1913.*

John Bailey (1833-1909) came to
Fort Mackinac when his father, army
surgeon Joseph Bailey, was assigned
there in 1852. In 1854 he graduated with
a medical degree from the University of
Michigan. He was appointed as an assistant
surgeon in the army and replaced his father at Fort
Mackinac. Bailey later served at posts in New York and
Minnesota, but left the army in 1858 and took up private
practice on Mackinac Island.

Bailey served with merit as a surgeon in the Civil War
and returned to private practice on Mackinac Island
after the war, also operating a drug store. Between 1866
and 1895 he served numerous times under contract as
"acting assistant surgeon" at Fort Mackinac. Dr. Bailey
was involved politically and socially both on Mackinac
Island and in the state. In 1903 he was appointed to the
Mackinac Island State Park Commission,
helping to preserve the fort at which
he once served.

Figure 67 A-B
Bailey Medical Kit
ca. 1890
1977.10.1
Mrs. Robert Bailey, John R. Bailey,
descendents

Figure 68
GAR Ribbon
ca. 1890
L 8 W 3
1998.00.10

The Grand Army of the Republic (G.A.R.) was an organization of United States Civil War veterans. The Mackinac Island G.A.R. post was established in the mid-1880s and named in honor of Henry C. Pratt, the last commander of Fort Mackinac before the war and father of 23rd Infantry Lieutenant Edward B. Pratt (see Figure 59). Members of the post included retired veterans living on Mackinac Island and active enlisted men serving at the fort. This badge would have been worn in mourning for a deceased member. It was found at Fort Mackinac among records left by the army.

Figure 69
Fort Mackinac Painting
W 37.5 H 23.5
ca. 1890
1955.200.1

This view of the front of Fort Mackinac from the ramp shows the soldiers' gardens and the east end of the village. It was completed by an unknown artist in the twilight years of the fort's military period. The sentry box along the fort wall shows the brown color scheme applied to a number of the fort's buildings in the 1880s. This color was not known again until paint analysis was completed in the 1990s.

Figure 70
Fort Mackinac Chair
ca. 1885
U.320

When Dr. Eugene Petersen arrived on Mackinac Island in 1958, he searched the fort for anything dating to the military period. Apart from some army books and plans in the Park Commission vault, all he could find was this chair marked "USQMD" for "United States Quartermaster Department."

MACKINAC ISLAND
AND
MACKINAW CITY

MICHILIMACKINACK

Figure 71
Michilimackinac
Seth Eastman. Published in Mary H. Eastman,
The American Annual, 79.
1855
L 11.75 W 10.5
1985.65.1

*The commission's collection includes numerous examples
of published prints of Mackinac Island dating from the
1840s to the present. This view of Mackinac Island by
Seth Eastman (1808-1875) depicts the island in 1820 with
1838 additions. The lithograph is based on a watercolor
done by Eastman which is in turn based on a view of the
island done by Captain David Bates Douglass in 1820.*

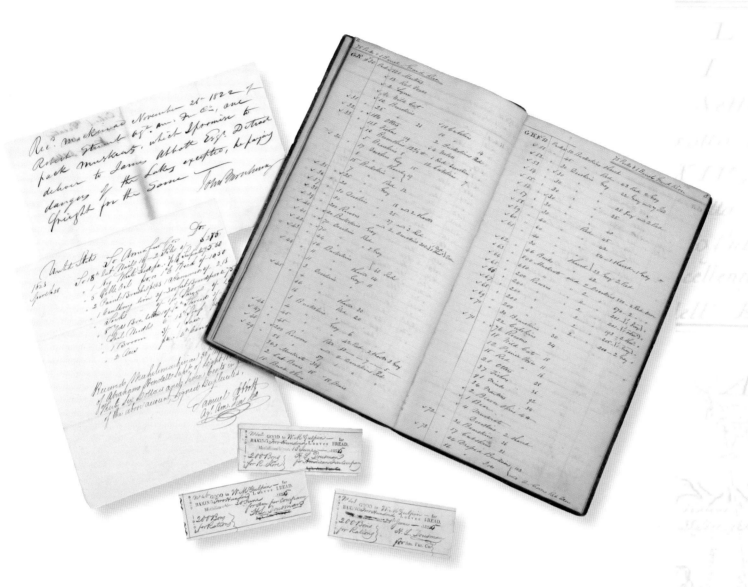

Figure 72
American Fur Co., Northern Dept., Receiving Book No. 1, 1834
Documents, 1822, 1823, 1825
Wendell-Fenton Archival Collection (AFC Organizational Records-1)

From the 1670s to the 1830s the Straits of Mackinac served as a center of the Great Lakes fur trade. After 1812 American merchants took firm control of this business, led by John Jacob Astor's American Fur Company. Company records are held in archives throughout the country. A small number remain at Mackinac, including record books owned by the City of Mackinac Island. The documents here are part of a small collection held by the commission, dating from the 1820s and 1830s. The small receipts at the bottom are for bread from island baker William McGulpin.

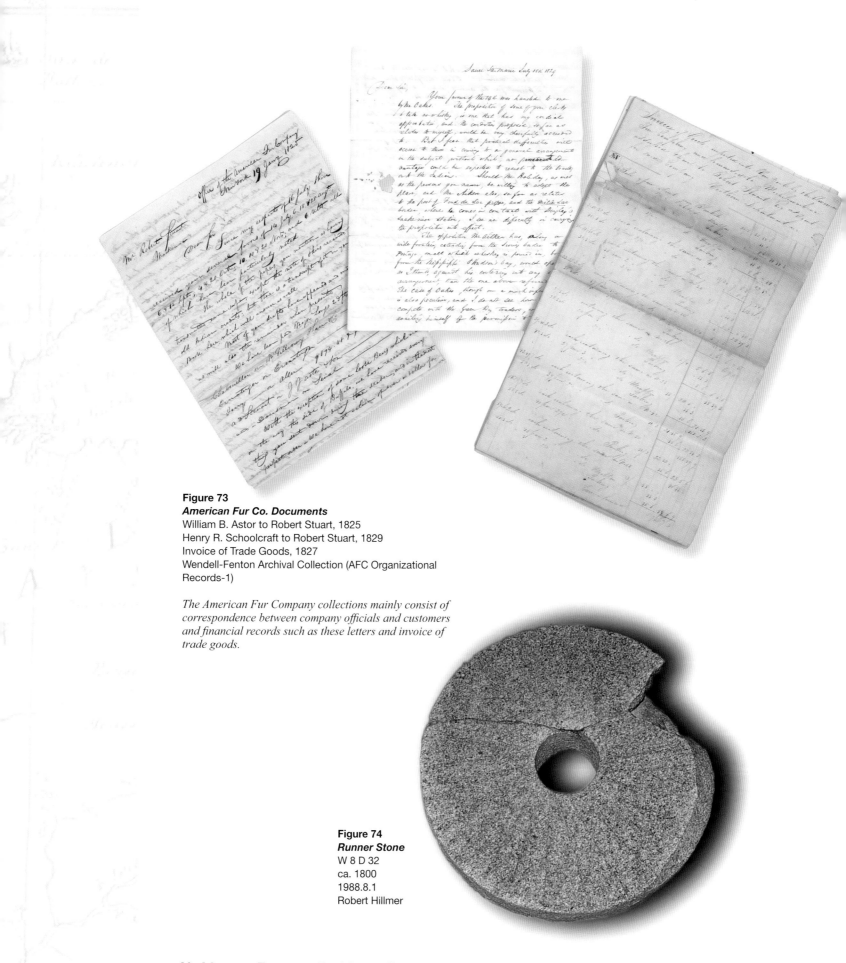

Figure 73
American Fur Co. Documents
William B. Astor to Robert Stuart, 1825
Henry R. Schoolcraft to Robert Stuart, 1829
Invoice of Trade Goods, 1827
Wendell-Fenton Archival Collection (AFC Organizational
Records-1)

*The American Fur Company collections mainly consist of
correspondence between company officials and customers
and financial records such as these letters and invoice of
trade goods.*

Figure 74
Runner Stone
W 8 D 32
ca. 1800
1988.8.1
Robert Hillmer

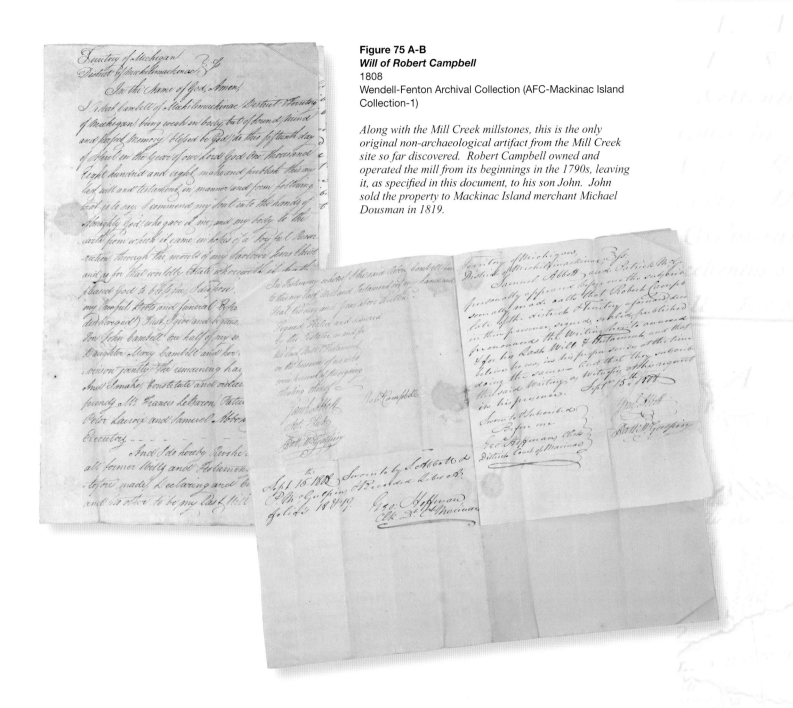

Figure 75 A-B
Will of Robert Campbell
1808
Wendell-Fenton Archival Collection (AFC-Mackinac Island
Collection-1)

*Along with the Mill Creek millstones, this is the only
original non-archaeological artifact from the Mill Creek
site so far discovered. Robert Campbell owned and
operated the mill from its beginnings in the 1790s, leaving
it, as specified in this document, to his son John. John
sold the property to Mackinac Island merchant Michael
Dousman in 1819.*

Opposite:
*This granite millstone is one of a pair that legend states came from Mill Creek. Robert Campbell had added a gristmill to
his sawmill operation at Mill Creek by the early 1800s. In 1860, twenty years after the mill was abandoned, the stones were
obtained by James Myers for use in his mill in nearby Cheboygan. He transferred the stones to his Myers Creek Mill south
of town in the middle 1860s. The mill ceased operation by 1890. In 1968 one of the stones, now broken, was found at the
Myers' mill site by donor Robert Hillmer and his father-in-law. The discovery piqued the interest of local historian Ellis
Olson and compelled him to search for the forgotten Mill Creek site. In 1972 he discovered the site with his wife, Mary, and
Margaret Lentini.*

*But what happened to the second stone? Apparently, in the early 1890s the other stone was acquired by Walter Watson, a
local farmer. It was taken by raft from Myers Creek down the Cheboygan River to the Watson farm south of Cheboygan.
Watson intended shipping it to the World's Colombian Exposition in Chicago. It never made it to the fair, but remained on the
Watson farm for the next century. In 1994 his granddaughter, Florence Bradstrom, donated the second stone (the bedstone,
1994.5.1) to the commission. Both stones are now exhibited at the site.*

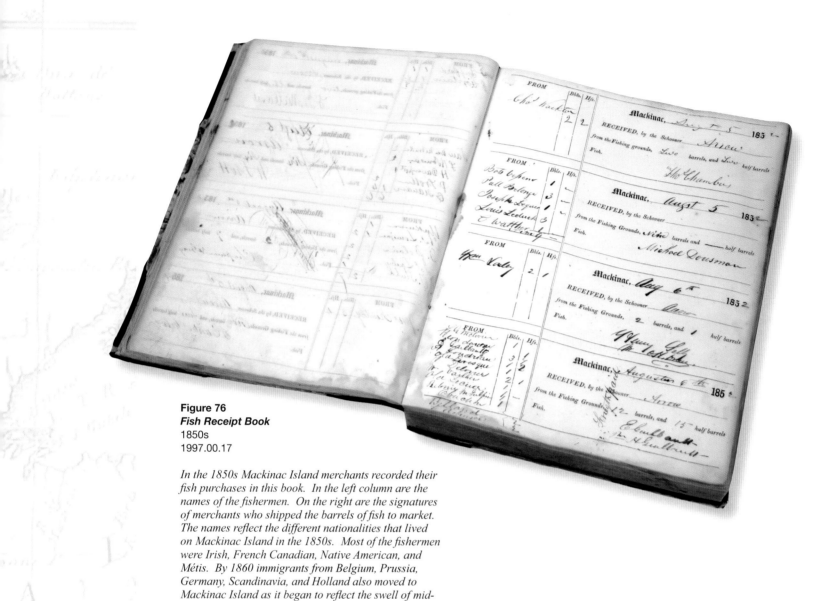

Figure 76
Fish Receipt Book
1850s
1997.00.17

In the 1850s Mackinac Island merchants recorded their
fish purchases in this book. In the left column are the
names of the fishermen. On the right are the signatures
of merchants who shipped the barrels of fish to market.
The names reflect the different nationalities that lived
on Mackinac Island in the 1850s. Most of the fishermen
were Irish, French Canadian, Native American, and
Métis. By 1860 immigrants from Belgium, Prussia,
Germany, Scandinavia, and Holland also moved to
Mackinac Island as it began to reflect the swell of mid-
nineteenth century European immigration to the United
States.

Figure 77
Fish Inspector Stamp
1974.149.1

*Iron stamp marked: "M. Geary Inspector,
Mackinac, Michigan." Matthew Geary was a
Mackinac Island fish inspector. After checking
the quality of the fish, he marked each barrel
with this branding iron.*

Figure 78
Father Piret Journal
1846
1955.1.1
Mrs. Brayton Saltanstall

*Rev. Andrew D. J. Piret (1802-1875) was born in Belgium.
He came to the Diocese of Detroit in 1846 and received
his first appointment to Ste. Anne's Parish on Mackinac
Island. This journal, with a picture of him later in life
attached to the inside front cover, records his journey
upon landing in New York in 1846. He served as dual
pastor of both Mackinac Island and St. Ignace for over
twenty years. In 1868 he retired from active work and
moved to Cheboygan, Michigan.*

Figure 79
Father Piret Silverware
ca. 1850
1955.2.1

*This modest collection of silver, representing pieces from
several different patterns, was owned by Father Piret.*

Figure 80 A-B
Communion Wafer Iron
L 33 (closed)
1973.497.1
Henry Murray

This communion wafer iron, used to make hosts for the Eucharist, is from Ste. Anne's Church. Ste. Anne's traces its origins to the Mission of St. Ignace, established by Father Marquette in 1671. The church ledger, preserved by the parish, dates to 1695. By 1715 the mission was relocated to the south side of the straits at Fort Michilimackinac. While the mission kept moving along with the Native Americans down the Lake Michigan shoreline, the Jesuits maintained a parish church at the fort, which by the 1740s was named in honor of Ste. Anne. The church building was the first structure moved to Mackinac Island in 1780 when the community was relocated. Originally located between Main and Market Streets along Hoban Street, a new church was built in the 1820s at the present location. In the 1870s this structure was replaced with the current building.

Figure 81
Photograph, Ste. Anne's Church
ca. 1895
1998.00.14

Ste. Anne's is today one of the oldest established Roman Catholic churches in the United States. The 1875 building was repaired and completely redecorated in the 1890s through the generosity of summer cottagers, island visitors, and the sale of the old church lot. This photograph documents the new main altar and reredos installed during that renovation, ordered from the E. Hackner Altar Co. of La Crosse, Wisconsin. Shortly after this photograph was taken the walls were covered with fresco stencil work.

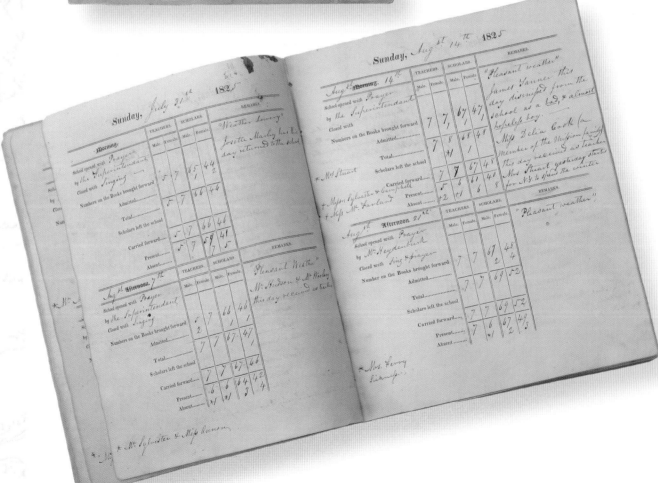

Figure 83
Rev. Meade C. Williams
by William H. Gardiner
ca. 1900
W 16 H 20.5
1972.739.1
Trustees of Mission Church

Presbyterian clergyman and Mackinac Island cottager,
Rev. Meade C. Williams had a deep interest in Mackinac
Island history. He published Early Mackinac: A
Sketch, Historical and Descriptive *in 1897 and was*
largely responsible for the salvage and restoration
of Mission Church in the 1890s. This was the first
historical restoration of a Mackinac Island building,
which preserved an architectural gem of the Midwest.
This original print by William H. Gardiner (see Figure
102) was ordered by the Trustees of Mission Church to
accompany a bronze plaque in Rev. Williams's honor in
the church's vestibule.

Figure 82 (opposite)
Sunday School Minute Book
1825
1955.217.1
Austin G. Packard

Protestant missionary William Ferry and wife, Amanda,
arrived on Mackinac Island from New England in
1823. Here they established the "Mackinaw Mission"
which included a boarding school for Indian and Métis
children. Within a few years a church (seemingly lifted
from New England and dropped on the Great Lakes shore)
was constructed next to the school. Both the Mission
House school building and the church are owned by the
commission and preserved as historic structures. In
this record book Rev. Ferry recorded the progress of the
mission's Sunday school. It was discovered by the donor
in a Massachusetts barn in the early twentieth century.

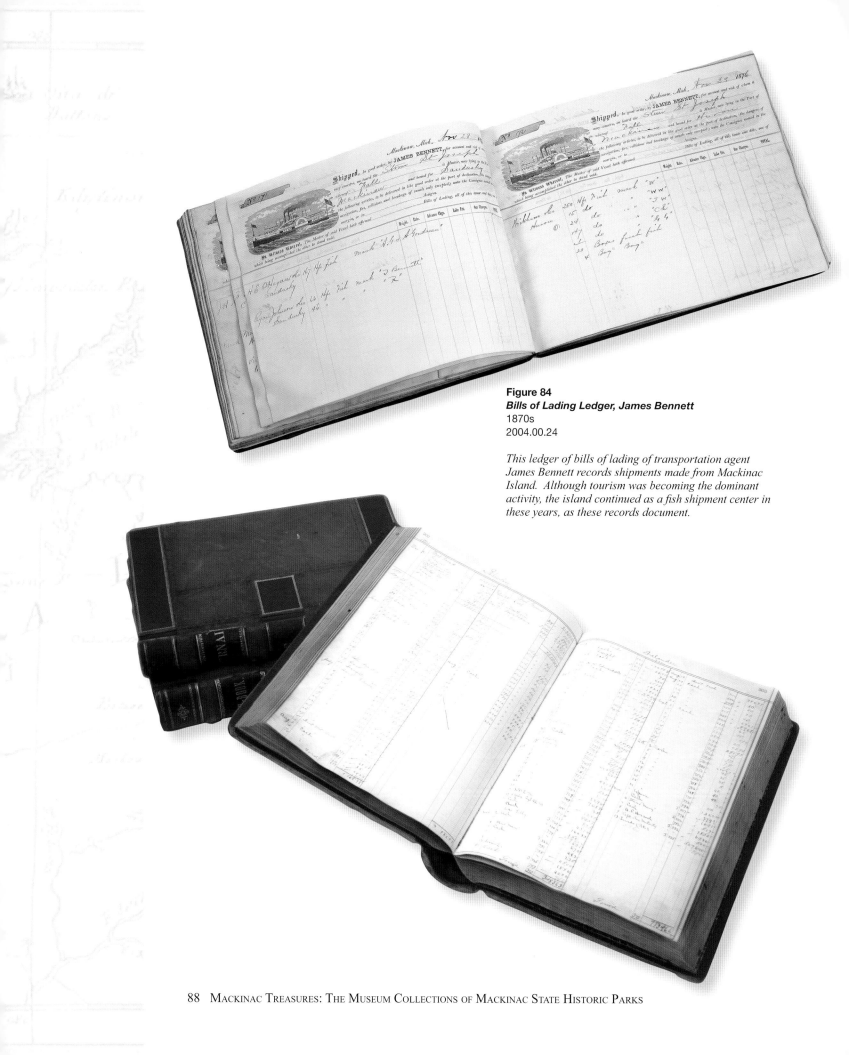

Figure 84
Bills of Lading Ledger, James Bennett
1870s
2004.00.24

This ledger of bills of lading of transportation agent James Bennett records shipments made from Mackinac Island. Although tourism was becoming the dominant activity, the island continued as a fish shipment center in these years, as these records document.

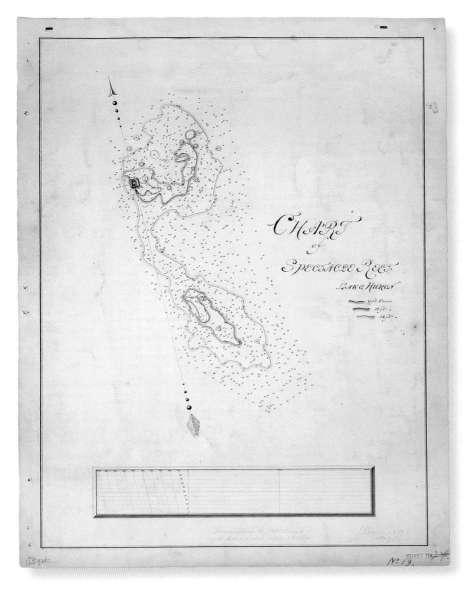

*The Straits of Mackinac,
an important shipping area
where all Lake Michigan
bound traffic passes, is laden
with numerous islands, shoals
and reefs. A lighthouse on
Bois Blanc Island in 1829
was the first lighthouse
established here. It was the
second light built on Lake
Huron.*

*Spectacle Reef is located at
the eastern end of the Straits
of Mackinac. It consists of
a dangerous pair of shoals
just seven feet below the Lake
Huron surface. The proposed
lighthouse, shown on this
chart, was built between 1870
and 1874. Its construction
was a major engineering
feat, with a massive crib
foundation making it the
tallest and most impressive
monolithic stone lighthouse
on the Great Lakes.*

*The Arnold Transit Co. was founded by George T.
Arnold and L. B. Coats in 1878. Arnold, a partner in
the Mackinac Lumber Co., originally conceived of the
line to move lumber around northern Michigan. The
company quickly expanded to carry a variety of goods
and, especially with the arrival of railroads at Mackinaw
City and St. Ignace, freight and passengers to Mackinac
Island. Arnold Line continues to operate today, the oldest
ferry line to Mackinac. The records of the company's first
decades consist of 25 volumes providing valuable data
from the time when Mackinac Island came into its own as
a premier summer resort of the Great Lakes.*

Figure 88 (opposite)
Light House at Skillagalee
Lake Michigan, Tower
1868
W 25 H 36
1972.808.1.39
James W. Jones

Skillagalee (Ile Aux Galets) is located at the western approach to the Straits of Mackinac in Lake Michigan. It is a small exposed portion of a large gravel shoal and claimed many wrecks prior to the construction of the first lighthouse there in 1851. This plan is for the 1868 tower at Skillagalee which replaced the original lighthouse. This was in turn replaced with a new lighthouse in 1888.

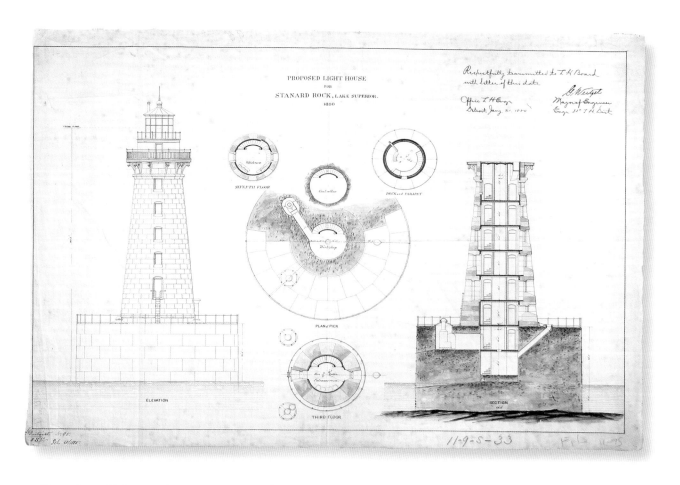

Donor James W. Jones and an associate retrieved these and other drawings from a dumpster in Cleveland sometime before 1972. The associate took the drawings for Lakes Erie and Ontario and Mr. Jones those for Huron, Michigan, and Superior. Mr. Jones was familiar with the commission's opening of the Michilimackinac Maritime Park and felt that the commission would be an ideal repository. He donated the material in 1972. The collection is comprised of architectural renderings and maps of various lighthouses and life-saving stations along the western Great Lakes. The bulk of the collection is on long-term loan to the Michigan State Archives in Lansing.

Figure 87
Proposed Light House for Stannard Rock, Lake Superior
1880
W 21 H 29.25
1972.808.1.64
James W. Jones

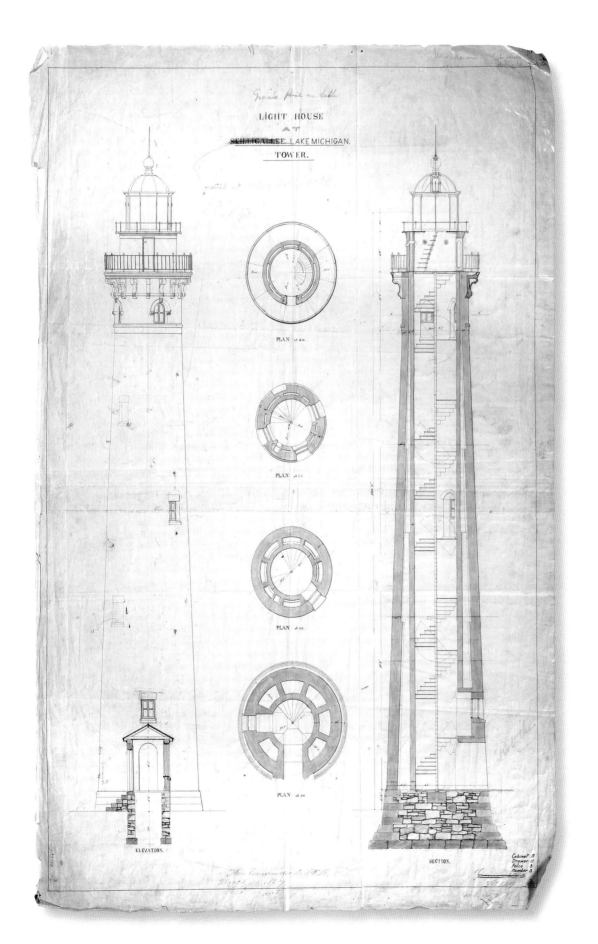

LIGHT HOUSE
at
SKILLIGALEE, LAKE MICHIGAN.
TOWER.

PLAN at aa

PLAN at cc

PLAN at cc

PLAN at ee

ELEVATION.

SECTION.

Figure 89
Frank Rounds Tools
ca. 1890-1930
1983.1, .8, .23, .30, .32., .43
Dale Gensman

Frank Rounds (1861-1945) worked as a carpenter-builder on Mackinac Island for six decades beginning in the late 1880s. With these tools he built summer cottages, worked on Grand Hotel, built the Round Island Lighthouse, made additions to Fort Mackinac, and fabricated boardwalks.

Figure 90 (opposite)
Hubbard's Annex Map
1882
W 24 H 18
Wendell-Fenton Archival
Collection (MIC-2)

Originally the farm of Ambrose Davenport, who came to Mackinac Island as a soldier in 1796, these 80 acres were purchased in 1855 by Gurdon Hubbard. Hubbard, who came to Mackinac Island from Vermont to work as a clerk for the American Fur Company, was dispatched by the company to lower Lake Michigan. There he became a pioneer of Chicago. Wealthy and influential, he nonetheless fondly remembered his days on the island.
He purchased the Davenport Farm and constructed a summer cottage in 1870. Beset with financial troubles in the '70s and '80s, and knowing of the clamor for cottage lots on the island, in 1882 he divided his parcel up into "Hubbard's Annex to the National Park." This is one of several plat maps in the collection, printed at the time to help promote the development.

Figure 91
Wicker Rocking Chair
ca. 1902
Heywood Brothers & Wakefield Co., Chicago
1996.70.4

Representative of Victorian summer leisure, wicker seating was the common furniture type in summer parlors and porches across America, including Mackinac Island. This example, resplendent in its original (non-painted) finish is from the cottage of Chicago attorney Lawrence Young, built in 1902 just west of the fort. Like the rows of cottages on the East and West Bluffs, this cottage was on land leased from the Park Commission (see Figure 172).

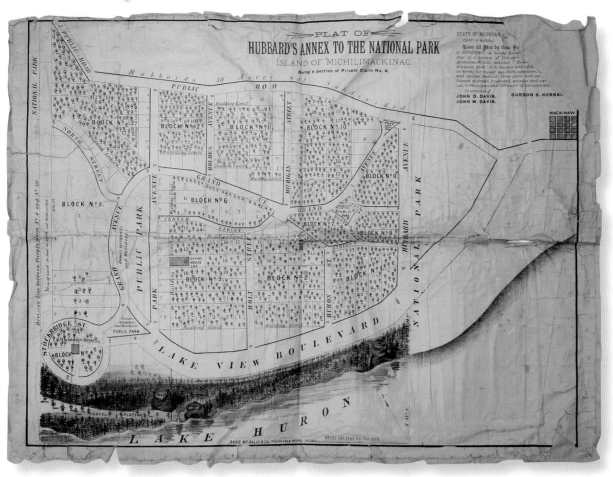

Figure 92
Tootle Documents
2005.28.1
Katherine Hannabass, descendent

*Cottage leases on the East and West Bluffs began in
the National Park period beginning in 1885. In 1897
Milton Tootle, Jr. of Missouri purchased one of the first
cottages built on the east bluff. He transformed the simple
Carpenter Gothic affair into an elegant Classical Revival
cottage. Tootle's desire for refinement was coupled with
his concern for modern convenience. A collection of
papers donated by his granddaughter documents his effort
to bring running water to the cottage (several years before
municipal water was available) via a private line and
wind mill on the shore. The documents illustrated here
demonstrate his effort to outfit carriages for the island.*

Figure 93 (opposite)
Untitled Painting of Mackinac Island,
Joseph Gies
1880s
W 21.25 H 10.25
2005.87.1
George and Stacey Hanley, descendent

*John Hanley (b. 1846) was a Detroit photographer. He
met Gies, also from Detroit, on Mackinac Island, where
Gies presented him with this color sketch. The view along
Water Street (Main Street) looking east features Fort
Mackinac in the distance and the Palmer House at the left.*

Figure 94
John Hanley Photographs
1880s
2005.87.3, 2005.87.4
George and Stacey Hanley, descendents

While Gies sketched, John Hanley made use of the latest artistic tool, his camera. Donated by his grandson, these are the only Mackinac photos by Hanley in the collection.

Figure 95
Arch Rock
1891
1998.00.16.2

Commercial artists discovered Mackinac Island not only resplendent with picturesque views but with tourists searching for keepsakes of their visit. Photographs of Mackinac Island began to appear in increasing numbers from the 1870s onward. Arch Rock was a favorite subject.

Figure 96
Sugar Loaf
1891
1998.00.16.1

Other natural wonders, such as Sugar Loaf, were also popular. Note the brave members of this 1891 party scaling the sides.

Figure 97
Photographs
Lover's Leap, H.4.8
Water Street, H.2.11
Grand Hotel Field Day, 1891, 2005.93.2
Mission Church, 1891, 2005.93.1

*The commission's collection includes over 1,000
individual original photographic prints. Most of the
earlier ones were taken by professionals, such as the
upper two presented here. The 1891 views at the bottom,
however, are amateur shots taken by the visiting Otis
family (see Figure 111).*

Figure 98
Stereoviews
Fort Garden, 1997.00.377
Arch Rock, 1997.00.328
Cannon, 2004.20.1
Island House, 1991.10.34,
Dr. & Mrs. Jack Willson Thompson
Ft. Holmes Tower, 1997.00.329
House of Anne, 1991.10.47,
Dr. and Mrs. Jack Willson Thompson

*A common photographic souvenir from the 1870s into
the 1890s was the stereoview card. The card produced
a three-dimensional image when viewed through a
stereopticon, found in nearly every Victorian parlor.
Mackinac views were produced by photographers working
at Mackinac as well as photographic publishers in
Detroit, Flint, Chicago, and elsewhere.*

Figure 99
Henry J. Rossiter Cabinet Cards
East End, 2004.113.2
Perry Cannon, 2004.113.1
Sugarloaf, 2004.113.3

Rossiter operated a photographic studio on the island from the 1880s until sometime between 1912 and 1915. He produced cabinet cards, such as these, as well as stereoviews.

Figure 100
Foley Brothers Photographs

Fort Mackinac Soldier, ca. 1890, 1997.00.404

Fort Mackinac Mortar Shell and East Block House, ca. 1890, 2000.12.1,
Pennsylvania State Society of the Daughters of the American Revolution
S.S. Cambria at the Dock, 1889, 2000.19.1
New Murray Hotel, ca. 1890, 2004.28.1

Opposite:
This print of the Fort Mackinac West Blockhouse with Grand Hotel in the distance was purchased by the Park Commission from photographer William H. Gardiner to be used on the commission's letterhead. The penciled markings were instructions to the printer for the type to be set under the image (the blockhouse was actually built in 1798). Gardiner, like Rossiter and the Foleys, established a studio on the island which operated from 1896 until his death in 1935. In the winters he shifted operations to Daytona, Florida. Gardiner produced scenic views, general photographic work, and portraits.

Edward, Reuben, and John Foley also opened a studio on the island in the 1880s. Like Rossiter they produced cabinet cards and stereoviews for the general tourist trade. They also provided group portraits at Arch Rock and of steamships (center). From their shop at the corner of Water and Fort Streets they sold a variety of souvenirs. They also did portrait work (upper left with an Arch Rock background). John Foley relocated to Petoskey, Michigan in about 1905, and operated a studio there until 1946.

Figure 101
Blockhouse Photograph by William H. Gardiner
1998.00.17
H.1.9

Portrait of William H. Gardiner
from original glass plate negative, ca. 1910
G.13B.347

Figure 102
Plate Boxes
1984.17.1
1984.124.1
1984.15.1
1984.223.1
Maria Moeller Douma
and Mr. and Mrs.
Robert Doud

The commission went from becoming a customer to the caretaker of the Gardiner photographs. In 1969 Deputy Director Dr. David Armour was called downtown to consider some antique photographic equipment and supplies, including these unused glass plates, which had been in Gardiner's studio since his death 34 years earlier. Stacked in crates nearby, and ready to be taken to the island dump, were the exposed and developed Gardiner plates. The over 4,000 negatives included views and portraits taken by Gardiner between 1896 and 1915 (and a few earlier ones from his days in Detroit). The Gardiner Collection, nearly trash, became one of the treasures of the commission's holdings.

Gardiner Hand Tinted Prints

One of Gardiner's specialties was the production of hand tinted photographic prints. This style of print had been popularized by Wallace Nutting in New England. Numerous photographers across the country emulated the Nutting style. Gardiner likely began producing his hand-colored photographs of Mackinac Island and Florida in the early twentieth century. The compositions closely resemble Nutting's. Each was inscribed with the title and Gardiner's signature "W. H. Gardiner" in pencil at the bottom. A few unsold versions came with the Gardiner Collection in 1969 (Figure 105). Since that time additional specimens have been acquired, including the others presented here.

Figure 103
Blockhouse
2007.59.1

Figure 104
Pine Point
2007.60.1

Figure 105
Sunset on the Boulevard
1987.114.1
Maria Moeller Douma and
Mr. and Mrs. Robert Doud

Figure 106
Arch Rock
1996.50.2a-b

Figure 107
Gitchie Manitou
1996.50.1A-B

Figure 108
Fort Mackinac
1987.113.1

Figure 109
A Colonial House
(1820s LaFramboise House)
1984.615.1

Figure 110
Clarice McKevier
Hand-tinted Print
ca. 1950
2004.9.4

Photographer Clarice McKevier (later Clarice McKevier Haynes) operated "The Studio," as her shop was called, on Mackinac Island from the 1940s into the early 1960s. She produced tinted photos in the style of Nutting and Gardiner, such as this one, as well as regular black and white prints, line art prints, etchings, and postcards.

The personal camera came to Mackinac Island at the turn of the century, allowing visitors to bring home personalized pictorial souvenirs. Many found their way into scrap books and photograph albums. Merchants catered to visitor's needs, as represented by the album on the right. Gardiner and George Wickman, who operated a studio and shop from 1899 until the 1940s, also sold cameras and Kodak film.

Figure 111
Photo Album
1905
2006.105.2
Photos of the Charles E. Nash family summer trip in 1905 from Chicago with images from Michigan, including Manistee, Mackinac Island, and Sault Ste. Marie, as well as images of the family aboard ship.

Photo Album
ca. 1935
2005.10.4
Unused album with image of a model of Fort Michilimackinac.

Photo Album
2006.44.1
Album documenting the Otis family's trip to and from Mackinac Island, ca. 1891.

Figure 112
Photo Album
1928
2001.37.1

This scrapbook includes purchased views published by George Wickman. The album documents the owner's eclectic trip that also included New York City, Yale, and Sault Ste. Marie, Michigan.

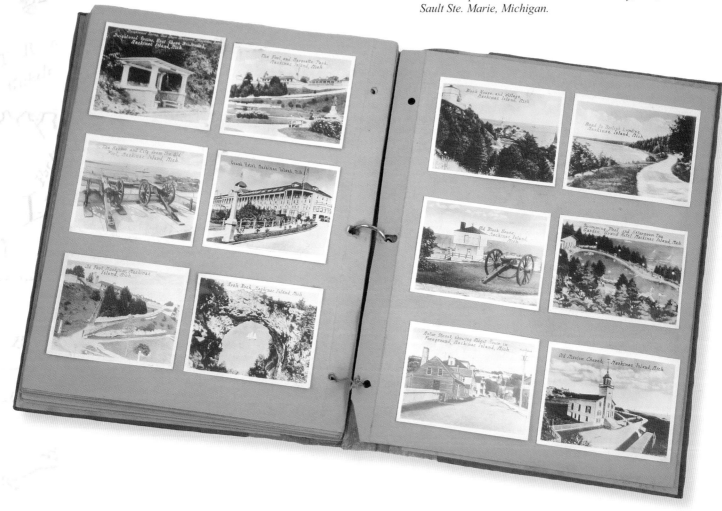

Figure 113
Snapshots and Negatives
1997.30.1
Tom Friggens

*This collection of snapshots, with their original negatives
and mailing envelope, document the donor's father's trip
from Detroit to Mackinac Island in the 1940s.*

Figure 114
Postcard Album
1907
2003.10.1

*The penny picture postcard came into existence in
1898. Mackinac Island proved a perfect venue. Local
photographers and national publishers printed views
of the island's wonders. Postcards were of course
mailed back home to those you "wish you were here,"
but collecting cards as personal mementos was also
popular. The postcard collecting craze peaked in 1910.
The Park Commission's collection includes hundreds of
cards, and more views are found every year. This album
includes cards from Connecticut, Rhode Island, New
Jersey, Minnesota, Mackinac Island, and Sault Ste. Marie,
Michigan. It includes thirty-two beautifully preserved
Mackinac cards, several of which were not known before.*

Prior to the arrival of the railroads at the straits in the 1880s, visitors arrived by water. Great Lakes passenger ships continued to ply the inland seas into the twentieth century, but in ever dwindling numbers through the decades, and ended in the late 1960s. These are examples of the numerous timetables, brochures, and promotional booklets produced by the shipping companies that included Mackinac Island on their route.

Figure 115
Goodrich Steamship Lines, 1916
1998.49.2

Detroit & Cleveland, 1934
1998.50.1

Detroit & Cleveland, 1898
2002.00.141

Seeandbee, ca. 1940
1997.53.28
Steve Voisin

Great Lakes Transportation Co., 1928
1997.43.3
Eleanor V. Hendricks

Detroit & Cleveland, ca. 1920
1998.47.1

Figure 116
Mackinac the Wonderful Isle
1997.00.305.4

**Mackinac Island, Michigan
Central, ca. 1885**
1997.78.1
Estate of John Fortier

**Mackinac Island, Michigan,
Mackinac Civic Association, 1927**
1997.37.1
Elizabeth A. Craig Brisson

*Railroads and island business groups
also produced promotional literature
about Mackinac Island. They came in
a variety of formats, both simple and
elaborate. The commission archives
contain scores of examples including
these three which feature beautiful cover
art evocative of their eras.*

Figure 118 (opposite)
Mackinac, Ancient and Picturesque by Gardiner
1997.00.305.8

Mackinac, Gem of the Lakes
1997.00.305.7

Mackinac Island, The Ancient Michilimackinac
1997.11.1

Mackinac Island
2000.33.9
Thomas Pfeiffelmann

*Souvenir albums of photographic views became
available by the turn of the twentieth century.
They were produced by island photographers
as well as regional printing companies.*

Guidebooks and souvenir albums featuring facts, figures, and images of the island's historic and scenic wonders were available once the visitor reached the island. On the right are two books produced by former Fort Mackinac officers (See Figures 57 and 67).

Figure 117
Mackinac Island Rotogravure
Accordion View Album
1997.00.163

Standard Guide to Mackinac Island
and Northern Lake Resorts
1997.00.305.2

Mackinac Under Three Flags
1990.5.1
Henry L. Caulkins Jr.

Annals of Fort Mackinac,
by Dwight Kelton
1998.00.11

Mackinac, Formerly Michilimackinac,
History and Guide Book,
by John R. Bailey
2007.21.1
Wynifred M. Jackson

Souvenir China

Souvenir means "to remember." A common practice of travelers is to bring home physical reminders of their ephemeral adventures. Souvenirs took on a variety of forms. Visitors to Mackinac often went home with stereoviews, booklets, and postcards. Among the three-dimensional variety were birchbark items, baskets, and glassware. Souvenir plates and pictorial china combined the two.

Figure 119
Souvenir Framed Tile
Minton's China Works
ca. 1915
1995.17.1
Ken and Diane Neyer

Souvenir Plate
William Allen & Co.
ca. 1920
1999.26.1

Pitcher
Adams Potteries, Old English Staffordshire Ware, Jonroth
2006.89.1

Earthenware souvenir plates and related tiles, pitchers, and other items were made in large numbers beginning in the 1890s. Most were produced in the first half of the twentieth century, largely by established English potteries. They resembled old Staffordshireware, already a collectible.

Souvenir pictorial china was produced largely by German firms from about 1890 to 1930. It was largely made of hard paste, white-bodied porcelain forms in Germany or Austria upon which engraved scenes were depicted. They dominated the market until the onset of World War I. Between the wars a diminished supply was introduced. The introduction of cheaper items from the Far East in the 1930s and ultimately World War II ended the era of German souvenir china. As represented in the Mackinac examples, there was a seemingly infinite variety of forms. Many of the views depicted were the same used on postcards of the day.

Figure 120
Porcelain Tumbler
2006.126.7

Pitcher
1996.49.3

Pitcher
2006.126.1

Cracker Jar
1973.234.1
Mrs. Paul Livelsberger

China Box
2006.13.1a-b
Cynthia Litzner

Pitcher
1996.33.1

Figure 121
Plate
1997.93.1
Marquette Park,
Wickman, Jonroth,
Germany

Plate
2001.52.1
Arch Rock; Jonroth;
"painted for G.H. Wickman
Mackinac Island, Mich."

Dish
2006.124.2
Wheelock; Made in
Germany for C.H. Parrott
Minneapolis
& Mackinac Isle

Plate
1999.24.1
Fort Mackinac

Plate
1996.46.1
Old Fort Mackinac; H.H.T.
Co. | Luckybuck Studios

Figure 122
Left to right:
Cobalt Blue Cup
1998.64.2.2

Cobalt Blue Sugar Bowl
1998.64.2.1

Vase
2001.52.6
Arch Rock

Cup and Saucer
2001.34.1a-b
Blue. Fort Mackinac;
Victoria Carlsbad,
Austria

China Basket
2001.52.5
Arch Rock; Wickman,
Jonroth

**Cobalt Blue Souvenir
Creamer**
1998.64.2.1

Cobalt Cup and Saucer
2003.45.2a-b
Blue; Arch Rock

Plate
2005.10.7
Blue; Mission Church

Blue Souvenir Plate
1998.65.1
Arch Rock

Cobalt Blue Creamer
1998.64.3

Pitcher
2006.109.1
White; Fort Mackinac;
Victoria Carlsbad
Austria

Toothpick Holder
2005.55.1
Blue; Mission Church

Figure 123
Custard Glass Mug
2000.21.1
Arch Rock

Custard Glass Tumbler
2006.5.1
Arch Rock

Custard Glass Mug
2006.133.1
West Blockhouse; scroll rim

Custard glass pictorial souvenirs were produced during the same period as German souvenir china. They often took on the same form and graphics, but were produced in the United States by the Heisey Glass Company of Newark, Ohio and its competitors.

Figure 124
Stoneware Mug
2005.10.5
Grand Hotel

Stoneware Mug/Stein
2006.14.1
Fort Mackinac

Stoneware Mug
2005.10.6
Arch Rock

Stoneware souvenir mugs are closely related to souvenir china and were produced in Germany during the same era by many of the beer stein producers.

Kriesche Glass

Frank Kriesche, a German immigrant from Bohemia, operated a glassware store on Main Street beginning in the 1890s. A skilled artisan, Kriesche imported German glassware and engraved it to order. Kriesche's shop offered a wide range of items including decanters, sets of dessert cups, bowls, beverage glasses, and stemware. These were used on tables of Mackinac Island summer cottages or taken home to towns throughout the Midwest. Kriesche also offered a variety of cheaper keepsakes to other summer tourists. The most popular of these were items with a ruby red coloring. Kriesche engraved these with the purchaser's name and date of their visit to Mackinac Island.

Figure 125
Goblet
2007.11.18.5

Decanter
2007.11.18.1

Tumbler
2007.11.15

Cordial
2007.11.18.3

High Ball
2007.11.18.4

These items are from the
Lawrence Young Cottage
(see Figure 172)

Portrait of Frank Kriesche
by William H. Gardiner
from original glass plate
negative, ca. 1900
G13A.440

Figure 126
Glass
2006.126.2
Painted image of Fort
Mackinac with engraving
"Mackinac Island, Florence
Sept. 4, 1902"

Glass
2006.126.3
Painted flowers just below
rim with engraving
"Thekla Souvenir from
Mackinac Island, Mich.
July 7, 1898"

Finger Bowl
2006.126.6
"To Brother Dunne from
Rebecca
Mackinac Island Mich
Oct 9 1898"

Engraved Shot Glass
2006.14.7
"Bimi Mackinac Island, Aug
7, 1905"

Stemmed Glasses
2007.11.17.1
2007.11.17.2
2007.11.17.3

*The stemware also
belonged to the Young
family and is engraved with
their names. The other
items were purchased by
island visitors.*

Figure 127
Starting at top, left to right:
Ruby Glass Mug
2006.14.3
"To Edna from Papa
Mackinac Island, Mich.
Aug 25, 1901"

Ruby Flash Mug
2000.24.1
"Mrs. Wm. Markhoff
Souvenir from Mackinac
Island, Mich. July 22, 1897"

Ruby Glass Tumbler
2006.14.4
"From Walter to Robert
Souvenir of Mackinac
Island, Mich
Aug 8, 1897"

Ruby Glass Tumbler
2006.126.5
"From Will to Anna
Mackinac Island, Mich.
Aug 16 1894"

Ruby Glass Pitcher
2007.54.1

Ruby Glass Tumbler
2005.9.2
"Nellie Mackinac Island,
Mich Aug 30, 1903"

Ruby Flash Mug
1998.21.2
"E.A. McFarland
Mackinac Island Mich.
Sept 4 1901"

Bottom:
Ruby Glass Small Mug
2006.126.4
"We, Us, & Co.
Mackinac Island, Mich.
Aug. 14, 1894"

Ruby Glass Miniature Mug
2000.24.2
"Mackinac Island"

Ruby Flash Mug
1998.21.1
"Thedor Ernest,
Mackinac Island Mich.
June 27, 1901"

***Ruby Glass Sugar Bowl
and Creamer***
2000.18.1
Purchase
"J.F. Ryan /
Mackinac Island Mich. /
Aug 13, 1901"

Ruby Glass Cup
2006.14.2
"Eight in our Party,
Mackinac Island, Mich.
Aug 20, 1896"

Ruby Glass Mug
2006.132.1
"Ida Mackinac Island Mich
Aug 22 – 1895"

Souvenir spoons were introduced in the 1880s, and took off in a collecting craze in the 1890s. Like souvenir china and postcards, popular subjects for the spoons included Fort Mackinac and Arch Rock, the latter often gracing the top of the handle with the arch pierced. The swastika, in the pre-Nazi era, was a symbol of good luck.

Figure 128
Spoons
Top, left to right:
1998.51.1
1998.22.1
1998.54.1
1998.24.1
2001.16.1

Bottom, top to bottom:
1998.46.1
1998.11.1, Carl R. Nold
1999.24.2
1999.22.1
1997.28.1
1998.22.2
1998.67.1

Cheap souvenir-ware from the East Asian countries began making an inroads after World War I, eventually taking over the market formerly held by German companies. After World War II the majority of souvenir goods came from these countries. These examples of mid-twentieth-century kitsch date from the 1960s.

Figure 129
Cup and Saucer
2006.112.1
Bethel Ebinger
Image of Fort Mackinac
with horse-drawn carriage
in the foreground.

Glass
1996.39.5
Frosted glass image of
Mackinac Bridge.

Glass
1996.54.1
Frosted glass,
"MACKINAW CITY, MICH."

Souvenir Plate
2006.111.1
Mary Jaeschke
"Historic Mackinac Island"

Chair Salt and Pepper Shakers
1999.37.1

Cup and Saucer
1996.57.4

Cup and Saucer
"MACKINAW/CITY, MICH"
1997.6.1

Blockhouse Salt and Pepper Shakers
1999.41.1

Toothpick Holder
2005.80.1

A collection of advertising and business cards from the 1890s through the 1930s highlight the fact that most trade on Mackinac catered to tourists.

Figure 130
Mrs. Stephen Doud's Boarding House,
1998.00.15.1

Locust Cottage, 2002.1.5,
Carl R. Nold

Benjamin Carriage Line,
1998.001.15.2

Dufina, Golf Pro,
1998.00.15.5

Fenton's Bazaar,
1996.35.1

James Gallagher,
1998.00.15.6

Chambers Carriage Line,
1998.00.15.4

McInTyre's Carriage Line,
1998.49.3

King Carriage Line,
1997.00.254.3

Lakeside Grill, 2005.8.2

Newton Carriage Line,
1998.00.15.3

Figure 131
Community Documents
Starr's Livery Ledger
2002.00.171

Mackinac Island State
Bank Letterhead
1998.00.18.1

Program, The Whole
Year 'Round, Children's
Cantata
1903, 1998.00.18.6

Program, Mission Church
Service
1934, 1998.00.18.7

Invitation, Mackinac
Island High School
Commencement
1903, 1998.00.18.5

Doud Mercantile Bill
1995.13.2,
Clayton and Ann Timmons

Municipal Power Co. Bill
1995.13.2,
Clayton and Ann Timmons

The archival collection holds a variety of materials
documenting business activity and community life on
Mackinac Island.

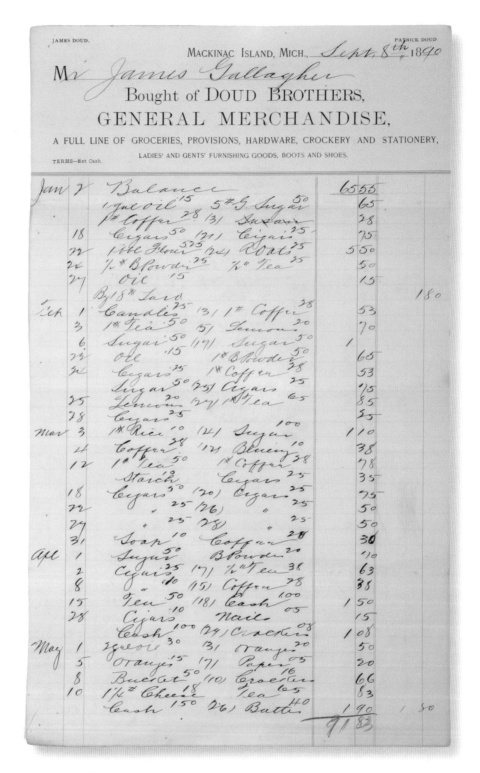

Figure 132
Doud Brothers Bill
1890
1998.00.19.2

Doud's Grocery has been an island institution for well over a century. More than interesting curiosities, the data provided by such mundane records can be analyzed to provide insights into many aspects of life in the past.

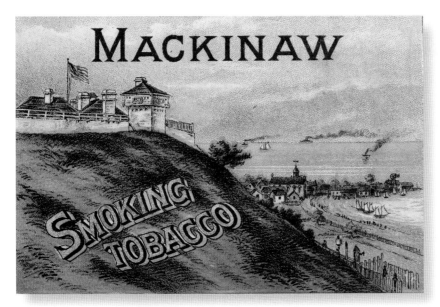

Figure 133
Mackinaw Smoking Tobacco
Trade Card
ca. 1890
2005.9.3

"Mackinaw" brand smoking tobacco likely did not have a widely dispersed market. Tobacco and cigars were produced in locations throughout the country and packaged for local and regional distribution. In a bit of lithographic ecumenicalism, Ste. Anne's church (which at the time had no steeple) and the steeple of Mission Church have been merged together.

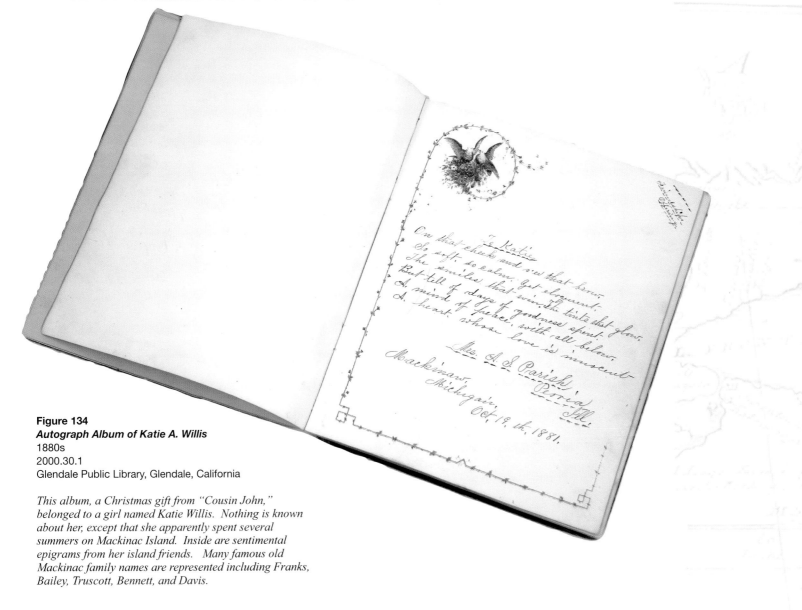

Figure 134
Autograph Album of Katie A. Willis
1880s
2000.30.1
Glendale Public Library, Glendale, California

This album, a Christmas gift from "Cousin John," belonged to a girl named Katie Willis. Nothing is known about her, except that she apparently spent several summers on Mackinac Island. Inside are sentimental epigrams from her island friends. Many famous old Mackinac family names are represented including Franks, Bailey, Truscott, Bennett, and Davis.

Figure 135
Lap Desk
ca. 1875
1995.10.1
David Truscott Dort

Used by George Bates Truscott (b. 1864) as a student on Mackinac Island. George was the son of George Truscott, born in England, and Sophia Bates Truscott of Ontario. The family came to Mackinac Island in 1866. George's sister was Rosa Truscott Webb (see Figures 52 and 53).

Figure 136
Grand Hotel Photo
ca. 1888
1998.00.16.3

Figure 137
Grand Hotel China

Grand Hotel was constructed by the Michigan Central Railroad, Grand Rapids and Indiana Railroad, and Detroit and Cleveland Steamship Navigation Company in 1887. It was not uncommon for railroads, in particular, to become major investors in resort properties in order to encourage people to travel. The first few seasons were difficult, but the hotel rocketed to success in the 1890s, becoming one of the chief Mackinac Island landmarks and icons. It remained open even during the Great Depression and remains one of the few great Victorian resort hotels still operating in America.

Dining at Grand Hotel is one of the key features of a stay. Over the past century and a quarter the menu offerings and china patterns haven changed. Specimens of early china are rare. The Park Commission owns the only two "PGH" examples known to exist.

"PGH" Soup Plate
1887-89
1998.9 (1-3?)
Hugh Mabie

The "PGH" stand for "Plank's Grand Hotel." During its first three seasons the hotel was known by this name, a condition of the manager John Oliver Plank. According to family tradition, employees were allowed to take home chipped china. This piece was passed down through the family.

Planters Hotel/Grand Hotel Dinner Plate
Syracuse China Co.
ca. 1910
2002.5.1

From 1900 to 1918 Grand Hotel was jointly managed with the Planter's Hotel in St. Louis, Missouri. The plate features Planter's Hotel Company logo in the center which includes two oval devices representing the Grand Hotel on Mackinac Island and Planter's Hotel in St. Louis.

Grand Hotel Salad Plate
Syracuse China Co.
1949
2005.54.1

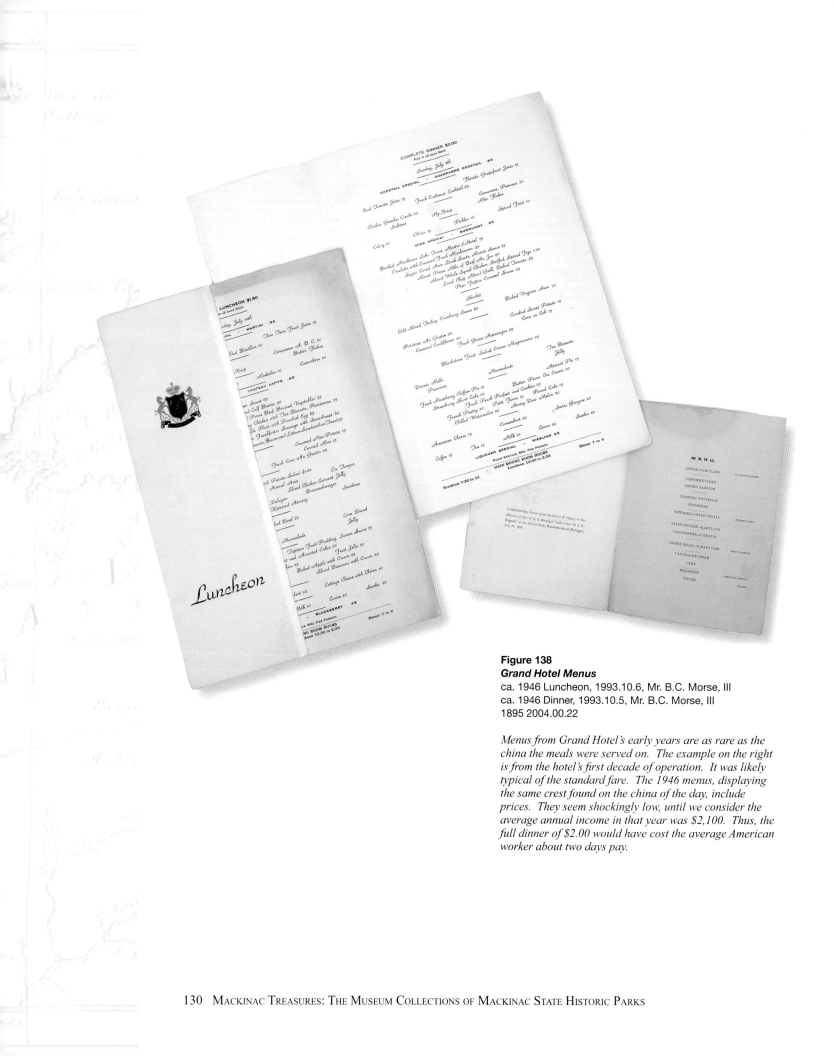

Figure 138
Grand Hotel Menus
ca. 1946 Luncheon, 1993.10.6, Mr. B.C. Morse, III
ca. 1946 Dinner, 1993.10.5, Mr. B.C. Morse, III
1895 2004.00.22

Menus from Grand Hotel's early years are as rare as the china the meals were served on. The example on the right is from the hotel's first decade of operation. It was likely typical of the standard fare. The 1946 menus, displaying the same crest found on the china of the day, include prices. They seem shockingly low, until we consider the average annual income in that year was $2,100. Thus, the full dinner of $2.00 would have cost the average American worker about two days pay.

Dinner

Cocktails

MACKINAC BREEZE .85
A tantalizing favorite of Creme de Menthe and Brandy
Grand Gimlet .75
Whiskey Sour .75
Manhattan .75
Martini .75
Old Fashioned .75
Champagne Cocktail 1.00

Appetizers

Supreme of Fresh Sea Food Cocktail
Chilled Melon
Tomato Juice
Cranberry Juice
Marinated Herring

Assorted Relishes and Preserves

Soups

Bisque of Crab Meat, Maryland
Cold Jellied Essence of Fowl
Clear Beef Broth, Printanier

Vegetables

New Broccoli, Hollandaise
Sliced Carrots, Vichy
O'Brien Potatoes
Mashed Potatoes
Steamed Rice

A 4

Entrees

Grilled Filet of Mackinac Whitefish, Lemon Butter
Fried Baby Spring Chicken, Country Gravy
Calf Liver Saute Smothered with Onions and Bacon
Baked Sugar Cured Ham, Glazed Pineapple
Roast Prime Ribs of Beef au Jus
Plain or Spanish Omelette
Dinner Sherbet
FROM CHARCOAL BROILER
Special Filet Mignon or Sirloin Steak, $1.50 Added Charge

Salads

Iceberg Lettuce
Summer Salad
DRESSINGS
Caesar, French, Mayonnaise, Thousand Island,
Garlic, Buccaneer, Roquefort, Horseradish

Your Selection of Desserts

Chocolate Cream Pie   Orange Layer Cake
Baked Cup Custard   Danish Pastry
            Cherry Jubilee
Ice Cream: Coffee, Butter Pecan, Cherry, Black Raspberry
Sherbet: Lemon, Orange, Lime
Cheese: Swiss, Roquefort, Camembert
Fresh Fruits or Berries

Beverages

Coffee, Tea, Milk, Cocoa, Sanka, Buttermilk

WORLD'S LARGEST SUMMER HOTEL

Wines

P. Hennequin, bottle 7.50
Vintage, Extra Dry
P. Hennequin, half bottle 4.00
Vintage, Extra Dry
Trouillard Rose Champagne, bottle 6.50
Vintage, Demi-sec
Prosper Vignal Sparkling Burgundy,
half bottle 3.50   bottle 6.50
Extra Dry
Liebfraumilch, bottle 3.50
Vintage
Moselblumchen, bottle 4.00
Vintage
Floria Argentine Sauterne, bottle 3.00
Vintage
Castello DiCanelli Italian Rhine, bottle 3.00
Vintage
Prosper Vignal, bottle 3.50
St. Julien, Vintage
Gancia Chianti, bottle 3.50
Vintage
Domestic Red Wines, bottle 2.50
Domestic White Wine, bottle 2.50
Harvey Bristol Cream Sherry, glass 1.00
Spanish Olorosso Sherry, glass .80
Portuguese Ruby Port, glass .65

Cordials

Cointreau .85
Cherry Heering .85
Grand Marniere .85
Creme de Cocoa .75
Creme de Menthe .75
Benedictine and Brandy 1.00
Domestic Brandies .70
Imported Cognac .85
Drambuie 1.00

Figure 139
Grand Hotel Menu, 1960
2004.138.4
John Webster

*Dinner in the Eisenhower era featured entrees of steak,
fried chicken, ham, liver, and omelettes ("plain" or
"Spanish"). This was not exactly fine dining in 1960, in
the style of Four Seasons or 21, but perhaps reflected the
bland palettes of the hotel's upper middle class guests.*

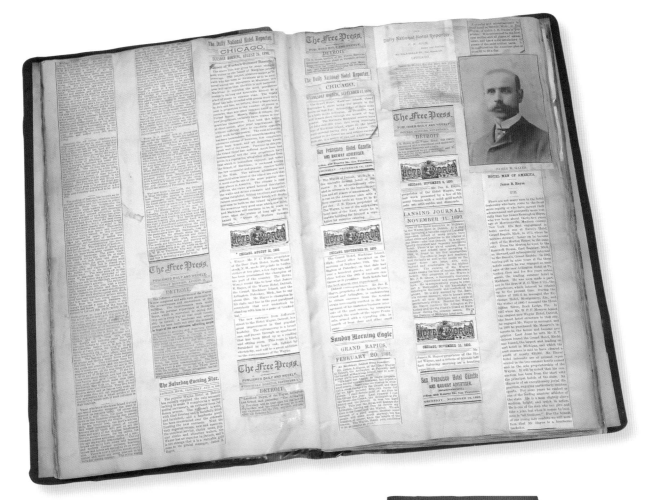

Figure 140
Grand Hotel Scrapbook
1889-1927
1984.628.1
George Bay

This is one of two scrapbooks in the collection made by James R. Hayes (1854-1927), manager of the Grand Hotel from 1890 through 1899. The books include clippings and memorabilia of his hotel activities, both at Grand Hotel, Wayne Hotel in Detroit, and other resort hotels.

Gum-backed stickers for a suitcase announced to the world how well traveled you were. Two of these unused examples also served as ads for the Chippewa Hotel, established in 1902. The far right one dates to 1947, when This Time for Keeps *was released (See 148 and 167). The M-G-M musical included scenes filmed on the island.*

Figure 143
Baggage Stickers
1940s
2004.25.2
2004.41.3
2004.25.1

It was not just summer vacationers, but conference attendees, that helped fill the rooms at Grand Hotel, as this 1916 program illustrates. The hotel stationery features both Grand Hotel and Wayne Hotel, operated jointly by James R. Hayes in the 1890s. The letter from Barney McDonald, head porter at Grand Hotel, seeks employment as a porter at a new hotel in Big Rapids. The brochure, announcing a new manager during the Planter's years, features descriptions and a plan of the hotel following a major addition and remodeling in 1912.

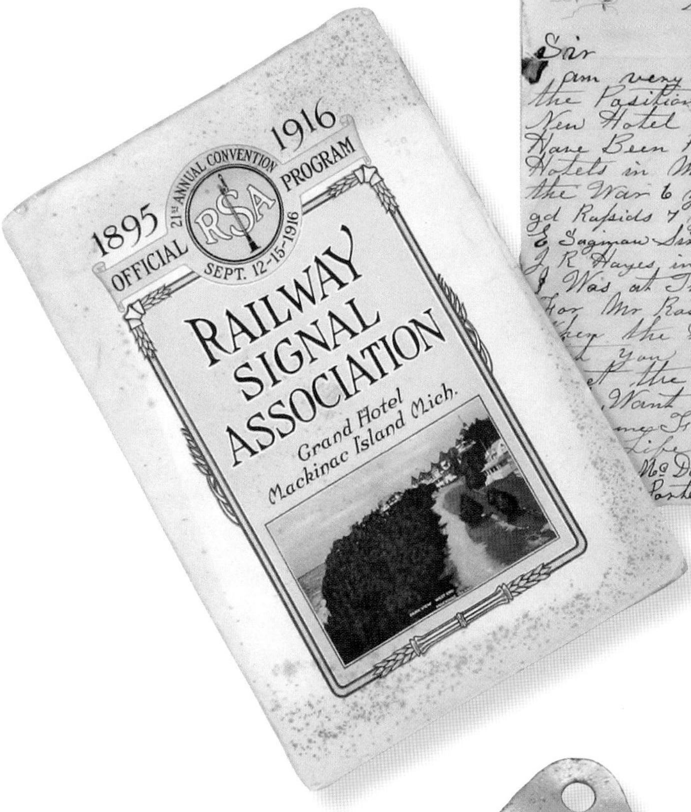

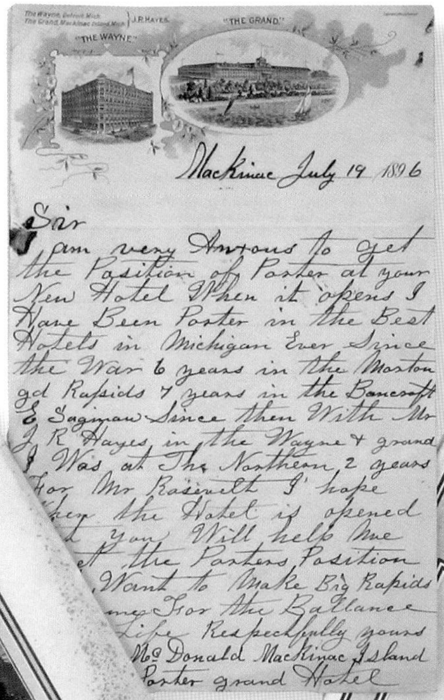

Figure 141
Conference Program
1916
1997.00.264

Letterhead
1896
2005.10.1

Brochure
ca. 1912
1997.00.263

Figure 142
Mission House Luggage Tag
ca. 1920
2004.41.3

The age of tourism dawned on Mackinac Island in the 1840s and 1850s. Decades before Grand Hotel opened, other resort hotels were established. Rev. Ferry's closed Mission House school became the island's first hotel in 1852. It operated until the Depression.

Since the middle 1800s Mackinac's main business has been tourism. Items documenting its many hotels are integral to the preservation and study of its history. These archival examples represent five of these. The John Jacob Astor House, like the Mission House, occupied buildings that had served an earlier purpose, in this case the former headquarters of Astor's American Fur Company. It was established before the Civil War and closed in the 1930s. The New Murray Hotel on Main Street still survives, but the New Mackinac (established in the 1870s but moving into a "new" building following an 1887 fire) closed during the Depression and was later torn down. The Iroquois on the Beach opened in 1907 and continues to host visitors. The Island House, today the oldest operating hotel on the island (although closed during the Depression), continues to occupy its original 1852 building with numerous additions.

Figure 144
New Murray Hotel Stationery
2003.26.1

John Jacob Astor House Stationery
1998.00.19.1

Iroquois on the Beach Brochure
2001.28.1
Bruce Lynn

The New Mackinac Menu
2001.00.190

The Island House Stationery and Envelope
1997.85.1
Dr. Edward Voss

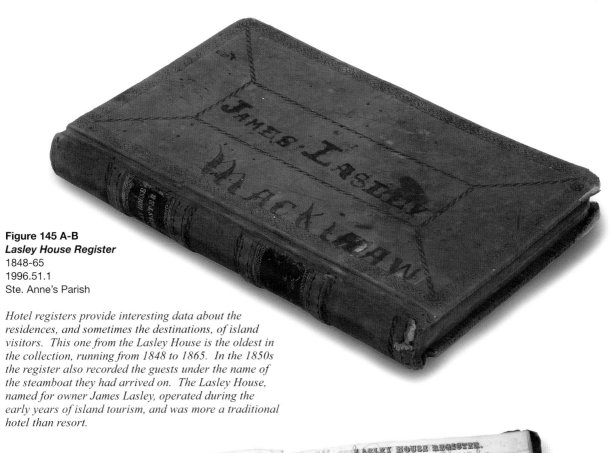

Figure 145 A-B
Lasley House Register
1848-65
1996.51.1
Ste. Anne's Parish

*Hotel registers provide interesting data about the
residences, and sometimes the destinations, of island
visitors. This one from the Lasley House is the oldest in
the collection, running from 1848 to 1865. In the 1850s
the register also recorded the guests under the name of
the steamboat they had arrived on. The Lasley House,
named for owner James Lasley, operated during the
early years of island tourism, and was more a traditional
hotel than resort.*

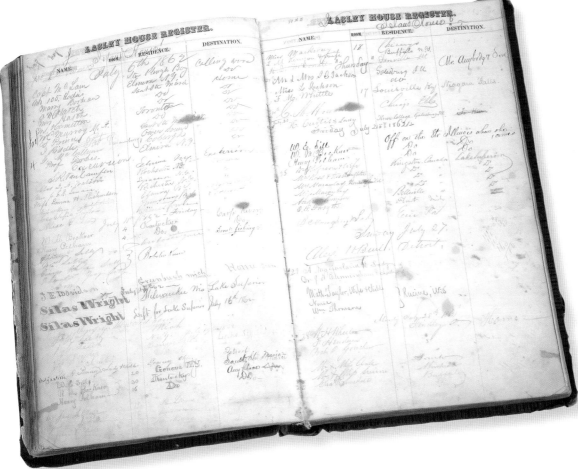

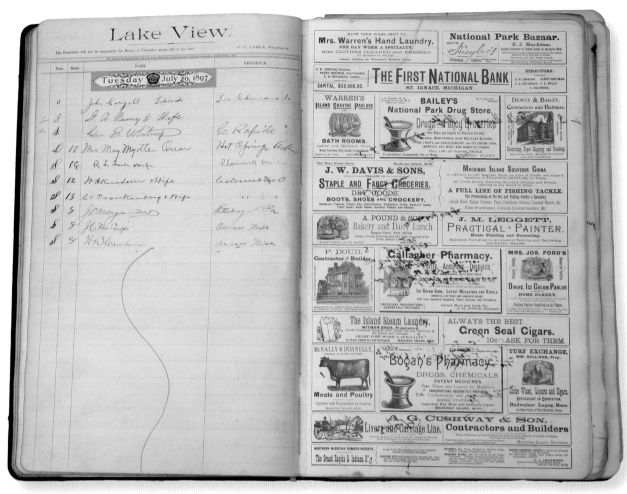

Figure 146
Lake View Register
1897
1993.9.2
Mr. B.C. Morse, III

The Lake View is still in operation at the corner of Main and Hoban Streets. Claude C. Cable originally owned the hotel. He was the son of James F. Cable, owner of the Astor House Hotel. Claude's sister, Jessie Cable Morse, was the wife of Lt. Benjamin Morse (see Figures 61-66). Beyond the names and residences of the guests, another interesting feature of this ledger are the blotter pages, imprinted with advertisements for island businesses.

Opposite:
Figure 148
Sheet Music
Left to right:
"Mackinac"
Words by John M. Morrison, Music by George Fraser,
Moral Re-Armament, 1943
Vern and Meryl Ericsson
1995.20.1

"Mackinac Island Waltz (Turtle Island)"
Words and music by Charlotte H. Brandt, M.A., F.J. Cusenz
Music Publishing, Co., Detroit, 1955
1998.00.20.1

"Spanish Waltz, Souvenir de Mackinac," Respectfully
Dedicated to Mr. Jas. R. Hayes, Proprietor Grand Hotel"
Len H. Salisbury, 1892
1984.628.1 (from Hayes scrapbook)

"When It's Lilac Time On Mackinac Island"
Words and music by Lesley Kirk, Robbins Music
Corporation, 1948
2005.26.1

*The island has inspired a few musical compositions,
none of them hits.*

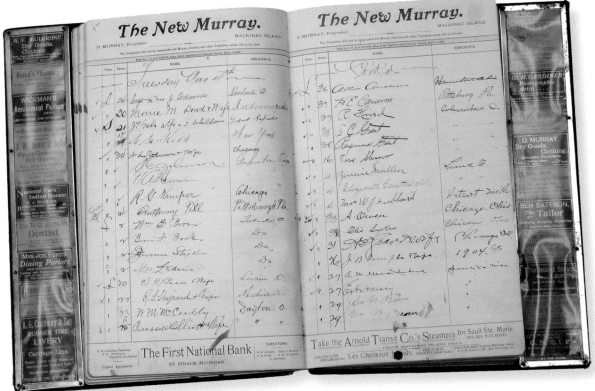

Figure 147
The New Murray Hotel Register
1903-04
2004.00.26

*The New Murray register also featured advertisements,
in this case on extensions to the covers.*

In 1895 twenty-year-old Mackinac National Park became Mackinac Island State Park, Michigan's first. Efforts to preserve the history of Mackinac include that of the Park Commission. Paperwork and publications originally created to manage the park are now preserved as part of the archival collection.

Figure 150
Park Commission Archives
Report of the Board of Commissioners, 1909
1997.00.305.5

Cottage Lease Bill
2004.139.6, Lawrence K. Keogh

Michilimackinac Park Permit
2007.18.1

Commission Correspondence, 1900s
Archival Collection (MISPC-1)

Cottage Lease
2004.139.3, Lawrence K. Keogh

Historic Guidebook
2004.63, Donald Libby

HIstoric Fort Michilimackinac Brochure
1998.58.6

Early efforts at preserving the island's history often focused on plaques and monuments, the most prominent being the Father Marquette statue. Efforts to erect a monument in the missionary explorer's honor date back to the 1870s under the auspices of the "Marquette Monument Association." This work ultimately dovetailed with the Park Commission's creation of "Marquette Park" from the old soldiers' garden in the early twentieth century. Chairman Peter White had been largely responsible for a statue of the explorer in his home town of Marquette in 1897 and worked to have a second copy created for the island. In his will, he left the final sum for the creation of the island statue in 1909.

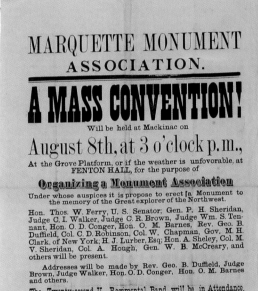

Figure 151
Marquette Statue
Statue Dedication Program, Mackinac Island, 1909

Statue Dedication Reception Committee Ribbon, 1909

Marquette Monument Association Poster, 1878

Statue Dedication Program, Marquette, 1897

Marquette Monument Association Stationery, 1895
Wendell-Fenton Archival Collection (MIC-2)

Marquette Statue Dedication by William H. Gardiner
from original glass plate negative, September 1, 1909
G.7.2

This Kalamazoo Company was capitalizing on the famous Mackinac name with this line of bicycles. Although the initial automobile ban occurred this same year, Mackinac would not be uniquely and famously the "auto-less isle" until twenty years later.

Commander E. M. Tellefson owned the cottages at Point aux Pins and Silver Birches. He operated a radio communications service at Fort Holmes for many years, as well. As a resident at Point aux Pins on the northern tip of the island, Tellefson found the ban on cars particularly inconvenient. He brought several vehicles to the island, in defiance of the ban. His cars were impounded and he was fined at various times. At one point he led a petition drive to have the ban overturned (and gathered an impressive number of names). Several of his vehicles remained on the island. This hubcap came from the rotting chassis of one of the cars abandoned at Point aux Pins.

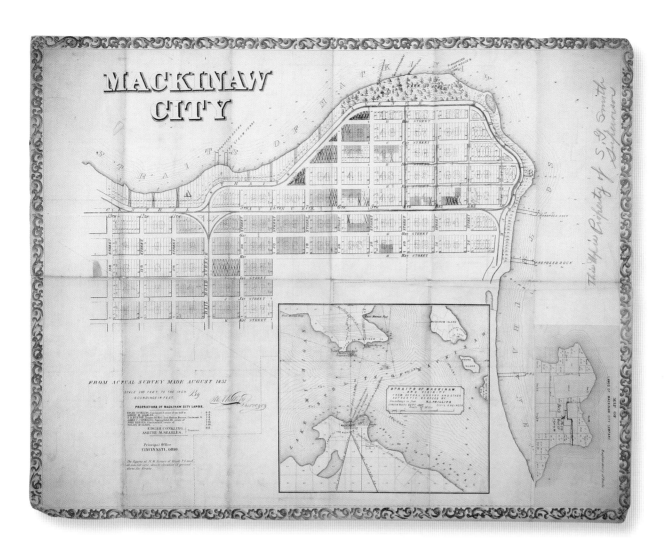

Figure 154
Mackinaw City from Actual Survey
Made August 1857
Robert C. Phillips, Lithograph by
Middleton, Wallace and Company
1857
2006.00.59

This map was issued as part of a pamphlet (coloring and inset added later) by Edward Deering Mansfield promoting the development of this as yet non-existing community. The booster of the enterprise was Edgar Conkling (1812-1881) of Cincinnati. The firm he founded purchased nearly 2,000 acres on the northern tip of the peninsula. It was adjacent to the location of old Fort Michilimackinac and the northern portion of the proposed village was reserved as a park. The town was surveyed and platted during the summer of 1857. The promotions and pamphlet followed, but purchasers did not. Mackinaw City would not come into being until the railroads arrived in the early 1880s. However, the town largely developed according to Conkling's plat.

Figure 155
Photograph, Mackinaw City Railroad Yard
ca. 1900
1998.00.13

This view looking west shows the passenger depot in the center distance.

Figure 156
Ship's Wheel,
Wawatam Railroad Car Ferry
1993.4.1-2
Michigan Department of Transportation

The Mackinac Transportation Company began railroad ferry service between St. Ignace and Mackinaw City in 1881. By 1888 they introduced innovative ice-breaker ferries. These ferries became models for ice-breaking vessels built around the world.

In 1911 the mighty Chief Wawatam *ice-breaker ferry joined the fleet. Operated until 1984, her career was a record that only a few vessels have achieved. The* Chief *incorporated much technology from the earlier ice breakers, but was built entirely of steel.*

Figure 157
Sugar Bowls, Sainte Marie *and* Chief Wawatam
Railroad Car Ferries
1974.94-95
Leona Brown

In 1913 the engines from the original 1893 Sainte
Marie *were used in a new steel-hulled vessel with the
same name, built along the same lines as the* Chief
Wawatam. *She operated until 1961. These bowls
are from the crew dining rooms aboard the vessels.*

Figure 158
Old Mackinac Point Lighthouse Plans
1995.9.1-3
Walt Plohocky

Figure 159
Olsen Lighthouse Uniform Sack Coat
ca. 1940
2003.13.1
Ray Olsen, descendent

Henrik Olsen served as assistant keeper at Old Mackinac Point from 1933, assuming keeper's duties in 1940, until retirement in 1951. He wore his uniform of the U. S. Lighthouse Service for formal occasions, such as inspections.

Opposite:
Established in 1889, Old Mackinac Point Light Station operated until 1957. A fog signal was completed in 1890 and the lighthouse two years later. Consisting of a tower and duplex keepers' quarters, the building projected a castle-like appearance with its Norman-inspired design. The station was surrounded by the village park platted by Conkling in 1857. The park was transferred to the State of Michigan and became Michilimackinac State Park in 1909, under the commission's care. The commission purchased the station property in 1961 and used the building as part of Michilimackinac Maritime Park from 1972 to 1991. In 2000 work began to restore the complex which reopened to the public in 2003.

Figure 160
Campbell Lighthouse Uniform
2003.40.2
Richard A. Campbell, descendent

John Campbell served as assistant keeper from 1944 to 1951 and then as keeper until the closing of the lighthouse in 1957. In 1939 the U. S. Coast Guard took command of the nation's lighthouses, transferred from a separate agency known variously as the Lighthouse Service and Bureau of Lighthouses and shuttled between the Departments of Treasury and Commerce. At the time keepers had a choice of remaining civilian or converting to military status, and Olsen remained the former. Campbell's uniform is of the Coast Guard type, a modified U. S. Navy regulation uniform, with distinguishing corps devices, buttons, and shoulder designations unique to the U. S. Coast Guard.

Figure 161
Farnsworth Console Radio
1939
Farnsworth Radio & Television Corporation
2003.13.7
Ray Olsen, descendent

This radio was purchased by the Olsen family in 1939 in nearby Cheboygan. It was used in their living room at Old Mackinac Point Lighthouse for the next twelve years. Today it is exhibited in the exact location where the Olsens placed it.

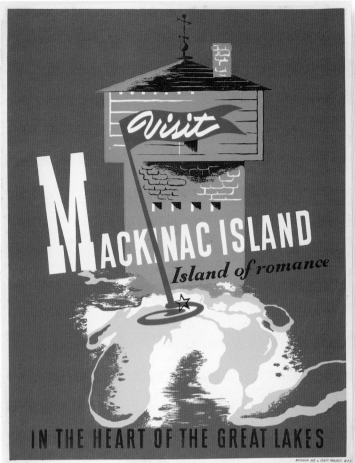

Figure 162
Mackinac Island Promotional Poster
Michigan Art & Craft Project, Works Project Administration
ca. 1940
1997.00.62

Paint on poster board.

Few people were taking summer vacations during the Great Depression. The City of Mackinac Island and the Park Commission did what they could to help lure visitors north. The federal government's Works Project Administration eventually assisted in this effort. Among the millions who worked for the WPA across the country were unemployed artists, working under the Federal Art Project branch. Several examples of their work are represented in the collection, including this original promotional poster.

Figure 163
Bas Relief Sign, Mission Church
J. W. Miximong, Works Project Administration
1997.00.424

Other examples of WPA artist's work on the island are hand-carved signs to mark historical structures. Each, such as this one for Mission Church, includes a view of the building and its name and date of construction. Several are still in use by the City of Mackinac Island today. Two are preserved in the collection.

Figure 164
Relief Map of Mackinac Island
Works Project Administration
ca. 1940
L 91 W 53
2002.00.321

This detailed map of Mackinac Island in wood, plaster, and foam was likely produced for exhibit at tourist venues to help lure visitors to the island. It is marked on the bottom with a WPA logo.

Figure 165 A-B
Franklin Delano Roosevelt Album
ca. 1930s
L 17.25 W 12
1998.30.1

Efforts to bring the president to Mackinac began with President Taft in 1911 and again with President Coolidge in 1927, the latter including an album of photographs. This album is an invitation from the State of Michigan to convince President Roosevelt to make Mackinac Island the "summer White House." This particular specimen was probably part of a 1933 resolution by the legislature inviting President Roosevelt to vacation at Mackinac Island. It is comprised of photographs of Mackinac Island, a hand-tooled leather cover, original renderings of the obverse and reverse of the federal seal, and a presentation statement. All were done by members of the art department at Michigan State Prison in Jackson with photos by the Department of Conservation. It is not clear if the album was ever presented, note that the signature lines are unfilled. It does not appear to be a copy (all text, including the photo captions and the seals are hand drawn). The Franklin D. Roosevelt Library has no record of such an album or invitation being made to Roosevelt. It was rescued from an office building fire in 1951. A smaller album of twelve photographs of Mackinac Island with a similar invitation was presented to Mrs. Roosevelt by Governor Comstock in 1934.

Figure 166
Scout Service Camp Patches
Left to right: 1998.10.5, 1998.10.7, 1998.10.9, 1998.10.6, 1998.10.8
David P. Monaghan

In 1929 the Park Commission, through the leadership of Commissioner Roger M. Andrews, established a Scout Service Camp on the island. Originally open to only Eagle Scouts and known as the "Governor's Honor Guard," the scouts served as guides at Fort Mackinac and helped in various other projects throughout the park. Future president Gerald Ford was among the first group of boys. In 1938 the program was opened to Boy Scout troops, no longer exclusively to those with the rank of Eagle. In 1974 it was opened to Girl Scouts, as well.

Figure 167
Lobby Cards
W 14 H 11
2003.59.1
2002.6.1

In 1946 Metro-Goldwyn-Meyer arrived on Mackinac to shoot scenes for the Technicolor musical This Time For Keeps *with Esther Williams, Jimmy Durante, Johnnie Johnston, Lauritz Melchior, and Xavier Cugat. Several winter scenes (with doubles standing in) were shot that winter and the entire cast and crew arrived for weeks worth of shooting in the summer. The lobby card to the right with Durante and Melchior is a scene in front of the Woodfill residence. Young Larry Keogh appears in the background driving his family's pony cart. The cart is now also part of the collection.*

Figure 168
Fort Mackinac Hollyhock Painting
Marion V. Loud (b. 1880)
ca. 1935
W 3.5 H 5.5
2006.115.1

Artist Marion V. Loud of Detroit spent several summers on Mackinac Island in the 1930s. She operated her studio in rented quarters at Fort Mackinac. This painting of the Fort Mackinac wall was, as the inscription on the reverse reads, presented to Florence Fuller who was serving as curator of the fort museum.

Figure 169
Portrait
Marion V. Loud (b. 1880)
ca. 1935
W 20 H 24
2007.38.1

This portrait of an unknown woman and wedding ring pattern quilt was part of commission property and used in a housing unit through the 1990s. It was likely painted on the island during one of the summers that Loud was here.

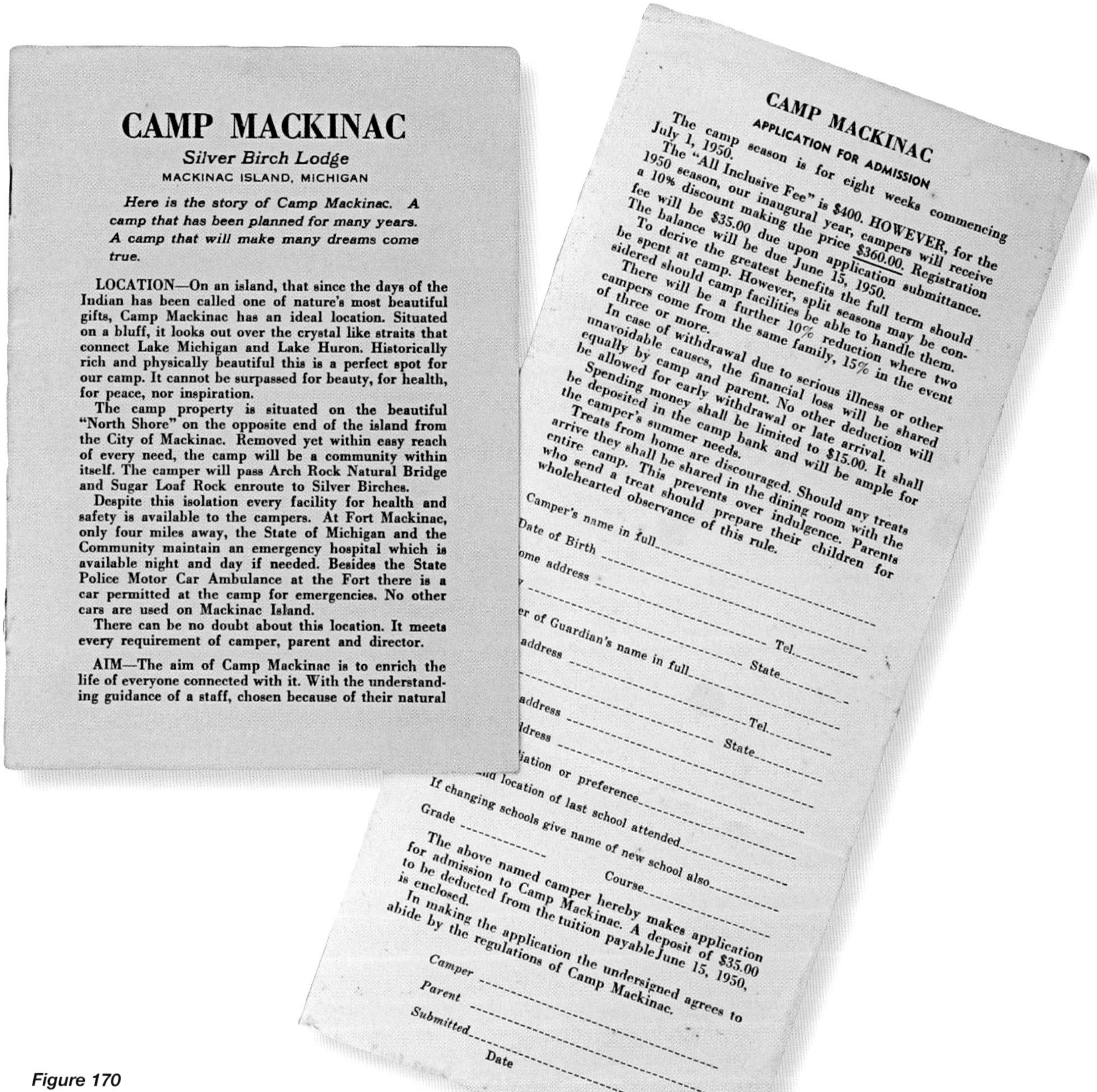

CAMP MACKINAC

Silver Birch Lodge
MACKINAC ISLAND, MICHIGAN

Here is the story of Camp Mackinac. A camp that has been planned for many years. A camp that will make many dreams come true.

LOCATION—On an island, that since the days of the Indian has been called one of nature's most beautiful gifts, Camp Mackinac has an ideal location. Situated on a bluff, it looks out over the crystal like straits that connect Lake Michigan and Lake Huron. Historically rich and physically beautiful this is a perfect spot for our camp. It cannot be surpassed for beauty, for health, for peace, nor inspiration.

The camp property is situated on the beautiful "North Shore" on the opposite end of the island from the City of Mackinac. Removed yet within easy reach of every need, the camp will be a community within itself. The camper will pass Arch Rock Natural Bridge and Sugar Loaf Rock enroute to Silver Birches.

Despite this isolation every facility for health and safety is available to the campers. At Fort Mackinac, only four miles away, the State of Michigan and the Community maintain an emergency hospital which is available night and day if needed. Besides the State Police Motor Car Ambulance at the Fort there is a car permitted at the camp for emergencies. No other cars are used on Mackinac Island.

There can be no doubt about this location. It meets every requirement of camper, parent and director.

AIM—The aim of Camp Mackinac is to enrich the life of everyone connected with it. With the understanding guidance of a staff, chosen because of their natural

CAMP MACKINAC
APPLICATION FOR ADMISSION

The camp season is for eight weeks commencing July 1, 1950.

The "All Inclusive Fee" is $400. HOWEVER, for the 1950 season, our inaugural year, campers will receive a 10% discount making the price $360.00. Registration fee will be $35.00 due upon application submittance. The balance will be due June 15, 1950.

To derive the greatest benefits the full term should be spent at camp. However, split seasons may be considered should camp facilities be able to handle them.

There will be a further 10% reduction where two campers come from the same family, 15% in the event of three or more.

In case of withdrawal due to serious illness or other unavoidable causes, the financial loss will be shared equally by camp and parent. No other deduction will be allowed for early withdrawal or late arrival.

Spending money shall be limited to $15.00. It shall be deposited in the camp bank and will be ample for the camper's summer needs.

Treats from home are discouraged. Should any treats arrive they shall be shared in the dining room with the entire camp. This prevents over indulgence. Parents who send a treat should prepare their children for wholehearted observance of this rule.

Camper's name in full _____

Date of Birth _____

Home address _____
_____

_____ of Guardian's name in full _____ Tel. _____

_____ address _____ State _____

_____ address _____ Tel. _____

_____ dress _____ State _____

_____ iation or preference _____

_____ location of last school attended _____

If changing schools give name of new school also _____

Grade _____

Course _____

The above named camper hereby makes application for admission to Camp Mackinac. A deposit of $35.00 to be deducted from the tuition payable June 15, 1950, is enclosed.

In making the application the undersigned agrees to abide by the regulations of Camp Mackinac.

Camper _____

Parent _____

Submitted _____

Date _____

Figure 170
**Camp Mackinac Brochure
and Application**
1950
2002.30.13
Tom Tellefson

For a brief period in the early 1950s Commander Tellefson (see Figure 153) operated a summer camp for girls at Silver Birch Lodge. These archival items are among the little surviving physical evidence of the short-lived endeavor.

Figure 171
Moral Re-Armament Collection
2004.63
Donald Libby

These photos and publications are part of an extensive collection of materials which belonged to Richard and Frances Hadden. The Haddens came to Mackinac Island with Moral Re-Armament in the 1940s. Originally known as the Oxford Group and started in England in the 1930s by former Lutheran pastor Frank Buchman from Pennsylvania, MR-A promoted peace and brotherhood among peoples. In the 1940s they made Mackinac Island their North American conference headquarters. Originally renting the then-closed Island House Hotel, MR-A eventually purchased the old Mission House lot and three large adjacent cottage lots. In the 1950s and 1960s they constructed a massive complex of buildings including conference and housing facilities, a theatre, and motion picture soundstage. Here the group held conferences with international attendees, rehearsed their plays, and launched "Up With People." By the late 1960s they converted their center into a four-year liberal arts college. It failed after four years and the center was sold, eventually becoming a summer resort, now known as Mission Point.

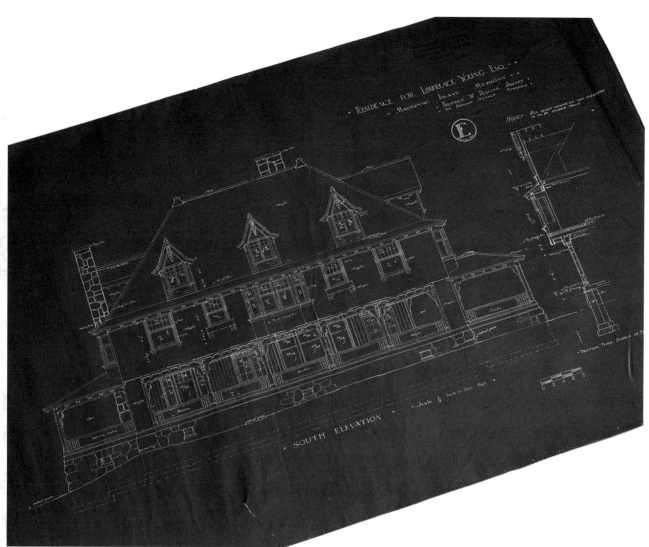

Figure 172
Residence for Lawrence A. Young, Esq., Mackinac
Island, Michigan
Frederick W. Perkins
1901
2000.00.75.5

In 1901 Lawrence A. Young (1869-1924) of Chicago
leased the West Fort Lot at the top of Fort Hill for a
summer cottage. The house was built in 1901-1902 from
the plans of Frederick W. Perkins of Chicago, who also
designed the Stonecliffe estate on the west side of the
island. In 1944 the commission purchased the cottage and
offered it to the governor as a summer residence. Various
governors had enjoyed summers on the island since the
1880s. In 1935 the Park Commission had made available
the former army officer's quarters nearest the fort to the
governor as a summer cottage. The Summer Residence
has been used by all Michigan governors since 1945.

Figure 173 A-B
Williams Silver Service
1950
2001.8.1-8
Nancy Williams Gram

*Silver service donated to Governor and
Mrs. G. Mennen Williams by the
Democratic Women of Wayne County.
The service was used in Lansing and
at the Governor's Summer Residence
during Williams's term (1949-1960).*

Figure 174
Straits of Mackinac Mural
Betty Beeby
1975
Oil on canvas
L 50 feet W 8 feet
2004.78.2

*In 1971 the Michilimackinac State Park Visitor's Center
was completed. The architects designed the north wall
of the center as a space for a 50 x 8 foot mural. Several
years later an artist was sought to carry out this work.
A number were contacted, but found the project too
daunting. Finally Dr. David Armour was put into contact
with Betty Beeby of Freeport, Michigan. She was more
challenged than daunted, and completed this mural,
showing the straits and Mackinac Bridge with winter ice
receding. In the clouds are images of Native Americans in
canoes. In a redesign of the center in 1990 the mural was
unfortunately blocked from view behind a curtain wall. It
was exposed again in 2005 and rededicated at a ceremony
with the artist in attendance.*

Betty Beeby painting the mural, 1974.

SELECTED BIBLIOGRAPHY

The information provided on the objects largely comes from the catalog information. This bibliography does not cover publications that were originally used by museum staff to document the objects. Listed here are only the works that were consulted to obtain additional information.

MACKINAC HISTORY

Armour, David A. "Mackinac Island Scout Service Camp." *Mackinac History*. Volume III, No. 1 (1998).

_____. *100 Years at Mackinac: A Centennial History of the Mackinac Island State Park Commission, 1895-1995*. Mackinac Island: Mackinac Island State Park Commission, 1995.

Brisson, Steven C. *Picturesque Mackinac: The Photographs of William H. Gardiner, 1896-1915*. Mackinac Island: Mackinac Island State Park Commission, 2005.

_____. *Wish You Were Here: An Album of Vintage Mackinac Postcards*. Mackinac Island: Mackinac Island State Park Commission, 2002.

Nold, Carl R. "The Michigan Governor's Summer Residence." *Mackinac History*. Volume III, No. 6 (2002).

Petersen, Eugene T. *Mackinac Island, Its History In Pictures*. Mackinac Island: Mackinac Island State Park Commission, 1973.

Porter, Phil. *A Desirable Station: Soldier Life at Fort Mackinac, 1867-1895*. Mackinac Island: Mackinac Island State Park Commission, 2003.

_____. *Mackinac: An Island Famous in These Regions*. Mackinac Island: Mackinac Island State Park Commission, 1998.

Widder, Keith R. *Battle for the Soul: Métis Children Encounter Evangelical Protestants at Mackinaw Mission, 1823-1837*. East Lansing: Michigan State University Press, 1999.

_____. *Reveille Till Taps: Soldier Life at Fort Mackinac, 1780-1895*. Mackinac Island: Mackinac Island State Park Commission, 1972.

MATERIAL CULTURE

Barnett, Le Roy. "Summer White House?" *Michigan History* 91, no. 3 (2007): 42-29.

Burgess, Arene. *A Collector's Guide to Souvenir Plates*. Atglen, Pennsylvania: Schiffer Publishing, 1996.

Conn, Richard. *Native American Art in the Denver Art Museum*. Seattle: University of Washington Press, 1979.

Emerson, William K. *Encyclopedia of United States Army Insignia and Uniforms*. Norman, Oklahoma: University of Oklahoma Press, 1996.

Langellier, John P. *Hats Off: Head Dress of the U. S. Army, 1872-1912.* Atglen, Pennsylvania: Schiffer Military History, 1999.

Peterson, Harold L. *The American Sword, 1775-1945.* Philadelphia: Ray Riling Arms Books Company, 1973.

Penney, David W. *Art of the American Indian Frontier.* Seattle: University of Washington Press and The Detroit Institute of Arts, 1992.

_____. , ed. *Great Lakes Indian Art.* Detroit: Wayne State University Press and the Detroit Institute of Arts, 1989.

Ottawa Quillwork on Birchbark. Harbor Springs, Michigan: Harbor Springs Historical Commission, 1983.

Phillips, Ruth B. *Trading Identifies: The Souvenir in Native North American Art from the Northeast, 1700-1900.* Seattle: University of Washington Press, 1998.

Rainwater, Dorothy T. and Donna H. Felger. *American Spoons: Souvenir and Historical.* Everybody's Press, Inc., 1977.

Straight Tongue: Minnesota Indian Art from the Bishop Whipple Collections. St. Paul: The Science Museum of Minnesota, 1980.

Williams, Laurence W. *Souvenir China: Keepsakes of a Golden Era.* Paducah, Kentucky: Collector Books, 1998.

ACKNOWLEDGMENTS

First and foremost we extend our thanks to the many donors, acknowledged in the book, who have made donations of objects to the commission. Many of these items were treasured heirlooms, and we appreciate the generosity of these individuals in parting with their family treasures in order for us to better understand and present the history of Mackinac. I also want to thank my colleagues and predecessors on the Mackinac State Historic Parks staff, noted in the introduction, who have helped care for this material over the years. In the preparation of material for this book, Registrar Brain Jaeschke deserves special mention for arranging the object photography and searching records for additional information. Thanks also to our Publications Team: Lynn Evans, Ron Crandell, Greg Hokans, Phil Porter and Jolene Priest for their careful review of the text and helpful comments.

Mackinac State Historic Parks has published over 100 titles since 1960. Over the last forty-eight years the Park Commission has supported this ambitious program. We are grateful to Chairman Frank J. Kelley and the entire commission for fostering these publications that provide an additional venue to preserve and present the history of Mackinac.

INDEX

A

American Fur Company 79, 80
Andrews, Commissioner
    Roger 8, 9, 152
Armour, Dr. David 12, 13, 101,
    158
Arch Rock 96, 98, 104, 116-118
Arnold Transit Co. 89

B

Bailey, John 74
Bailey, John R. 74, 113
Bailey, Mrs. Robert 44, 74
Baldwin, Mrs. Robert 43
Bay, George 132
Beach, Abbie Munger 53
Beaumont and St. Martin 54, 55
Beeby, Betty 158
Bellin, Jacques Nicolas 23, 27
Bennett, James 88
Bloswick, Clark 31
Bond, Mrs. James T. 67
Bowling, Violet 69
Bradstrom, Florence 81
Brisson, Elizabeth A. Craig 112
Brisson, Steven 16, 166
Brown, Leona 144

C

Camp Mackinac 154
Campbell, John 146
Campbell, Richard A. 146
Campbell, Robert 81
Carver, Jonathan 25
Caulkins, Henry L. Jr., 113
Chief Wawatam 143, 144
Chippewa Hotel 132
Conkling, Edgar 141
Corbusier, Harold 69
Cornwell, Dean 54, 55
Coronelli 20

D

D'Anville 24
Dakota 38
Dashwood, William 31
Davis, Caleb F. 33
Deed to Mackinac Island 12, 30

DeLisle, Guillaume 21
DePeyster, Arent Schuyler 29
Dickson, Mrs. Fred 33
Dillon, Richard 31
Dodge Brothers 140
Dort, David Truscott 64, 128
Doud, Mr. and Mrs. Robert 101,
    104
Douma, Maria Moeller 101, 104
Drew, Ella A. 53
Dunnigan, Brian 13

E

Eastman, Seth 78
Ebinger, Bethel 123
Ericsson, Vern and Meryl 136

F

Federico, Jean Taylor 31
Fenton, Charles B. 50
Fenlon, Joseph 44
Ferry, Amanda 32
Fletcher, John 65
Fletcher, Robert J. 65, 66
Foley Brothers 100
Fortier, John, Estate of 112
Francis, Donald 16
Freeland, Luna 53
Friggens, Tom 109
Fritz, Bill 15, 16

G

Gardiner, William H. 12, 87,
    100-107, 112, 119, 139
Geary, Matthew 82
Gensman, Dale 92
Gies, Joseph 94
Gilbert, Grove Shelden 56
Gilbert, Henry C. 38-42, 45-47
Glendale Public Library 127
Gram, Nancy Williams 157
Grand Army of the Republic
    (G.A.R.) 75
Grand Hotel 92, 118, 128-130,
    132, 133, 136
Gringhuis, Dirk 10
Groehn, Beulah 12

H

Hamilton, Marsha 15
Hanley, John 94, 95
Hanley, George and Stacey 94,
    95
Hannabass, Katherine 94
Harburn, Todd 31
Haring, Samuel Kipp 43
Hayes, James R. 132, 133, 136
Heintz, Henry 62, 63
Hendricks, Eleanor V. 111
Hillmer, Robert 80
Hill, Michelle 16
Hill Quarters 63
Hogg, Victor 10
Hubbard's Annex 92
Huthwaite, Bart 31

I

Imhoff, Vada 48
Iroquois on the Beach 134
Island House 98, 134, 155

J

Jackson, Wynifred M. 113
Jaeschke, Brian 16
Jaeschke, Mary 123
Jahn, Martin and Patricia 18, 20,
    21, 22, 23, 24, 25, 30, 31
John Jacob Astor House 70, 134,
    136
Jones, James W. 90

K

Kelton, Dwight H. 67, 68, 113
Kendall-Krapill, Kay 52
Keogh, Larry 138, 152
Kriesche, Frank 119

L

L. A. Lahontan 26
Lake View 136
Lasley House 135
Libby, Donald 138, 155
Lis, Jennifer 16
Litzner, Cynthia 115
Livelsberger, Mrs. Paul 115
Loud, Marion V. 152, 153
Lynn, Bruce 134

M

Mabie, Hugh 129
Mackinac Associates 56
Mackinaw City 48, 123, 141, 142
Mackinac Island Community Foundation 31
Mackinaw Mission 32, 38, 87
Mansfield, Edward Deering 141
Marquette Monument Association 139
Marquette Statue 139
Marshall, William 61
McDovall,Robert C. 131
McGrew, Albert D. 44
McKevier Haynes, Clarice 106
Menner, Elizabeth 50
Michigan Department of Natural Resources 52
Michigan Department of Transportation 143
Mission Church 10, 87, 97, 117, 125, 148
Mission Church, Trustees of 32, 87
Mission House 133, 155
Miximong, J. W. 148
Monaghan, David P. 151
Moral Re-Armament 136, 155
Morse, B. C. 70, 71, 130, 136
Morse, Benjamin Clarke, Jr 70-73, 136
Morse, William 71, 72
Mullet, John 28
Munger Drum 53
Murray, Henry 85

N

Nash family, Charles E. 107
New Mackinac 134
New Murray Hotel 100, 134, 137
Neyer, Ken and Diane 114
Nold, Carl 15, 17, 31, 122, 124
Norton, Cynthia 49
Nurmi, Linnea Aukee 16, 17

O

O'Brien, Charlotte 59, 60
O'Brien, John 59, 60
Odawa 36, 43, 45, 46
Ojibwa 38, 40-47

Old Mackinac Point Lighthouse 144-147
Olsen, Henrik 145
Olsen, Ray 145, 147
Olson, Ellis 81
Oshoga 40
Otis family 97, 107

P

Packard, Austin G. 87
Pamperin, David 15, 16
Pennsylvania State Society of the Daughters of the American Revolution 100
Perkins, Frederick W. 156
Perry Cannon 52, 99
Petersen, Dr. Eugene T. 10-12, 76
Petersen, Marion 10
Pfeiffelmann, Thomas 112
Phillips, Robert C. 141
Piret, Rev. Andrew D. J. 83, 84
Plohocky, Walt 144
Popple, Henry 22
Porter, Joseph 69
Porter, Phil 14, 17, 18, 31
Porter Hanks Sword 12, 52
Pratt, Lieutenant Edward 69, 75
Price, Margaret 9, 10

R

Robinson, Jane 15
Roosevelt, Franklin Delano 150
Rossiter, Henry J. 99
Rounds, Frank 92

S

Sainte Marie 144
Saltanstall, Mrs. Brayton 83
Santigo, Chief 44
Schlussel, Mark E. 31
Scout Service Camp Patches 151
Sergeants' Quarters 63, 65
Skillagalee 90
Spectacle Reef 89
Stannard Rock 90
Stark, Mrs. Birdie 43
Ste. Anne's Church 85, 86, 135
Stone Quarters 62
Stone Quarters museum 4, 6-8, 11
Sugar Loaf 89, 96

T

Tellefson, E. M. 140, 154
Tellefson, Tom 140, 154
Teysen, Kenneth 89
This Time For Keeps 132, 137, 152
Thompson, Dr. & Mrs. Jack Willson 98
Timmons, Clayton & Ann 28, 125
Tompkins, Budd 39, 41, 46, 47
Tootle, Milton Jr. 94
Treaty of La Pointe 38, 40-42, 45-47
Truscott, George Bates 128

U

Union Terminal Piers 89

V

Voss, Dr. Edward 134

W

Webb Silver Service 64
Webster, John 131
Whistler, Major William 56, 57
White, Hannah 32
Widder, Keith 13, 14
Wickman, George 107, 108, 116, 117
Williams, Governor G. Mennen 10, 157
Williams, Rev. Meade C. 87
Willis, Katie A. 127
Withington, Paul Douglas 55
Wood, Edwin O. 2, 4, 5, 9
Woodfill, W. Stewart 10
Woodward, Charles L. 42, 45, 47
Works Project Administration 49, 148, 149

Y

Young, Lawrence 93
Young (Lawrence A.) Cottage 93, 119, 156
Young, O'Brien Nicholas 59, 60

THE AUTHOR

A sixth-generation native of Michigan's Upper Peninsula, Steven Brisson received a B.A. in History from Northern Michigan University in 1989 and an M.A. from the Cooperstown Graduate Program in History Museum Studies in 1992. His museum career began as a student assistant with the Michigan Bureau of History at the Michigan Iron Industry Museum and Fayette Historic Townsite and at the Marquette County Historical Society.

He completed a senior internship at the Henry Ford Museum & Greenfield Village in 1991. He served as a curator for the State Historical Society of Wisconsin Sites Division from 1992 through 1995. In 1996 he accepted the position of Curator of Collections for Mackinac State Historic Parks and was appointed Chief Curator in 2004. He lives with his wife Lisa Craig Brisson, daughter Emma and sons Matthew and Andrew in Cheboygan.